KENNEDY

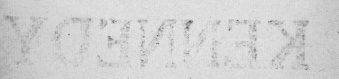

FAMOUS MYSTERIES

OF THE SEA

FAMOUS MYSTERIES

OF THE SEA

by

Patricia Lauber

DRAWINGS BY LEWIS ZACKS

THOMAS NELSON & SONS
Edinburgh NEW YORK *Toronto*

Contents

ASIATIC PRINCE
Hawaiian Islands

New Guinea

MISS EARHART'S PLANE
Howland Island

New Zealand

GENERAL GRANT
Auckland Islands

Secrets of the Cavern

BELOW New Zealand, in the far south of the world, a handful of tiny islands lies scattered in the Pacific. No one lives there, for the islands are scarcely more than outcroppings of rock. Bleak, wind-swept, and lonely, they are pinpoints in a mighty ocean. Their only visitors are scientists and the men who hunt whales and seals.

In the days of sailing ships, however, the islands were a more familiar sight. They lay near a route taken by ships traveling between Australia and England. Here both winds and currents carried ships forward on the long voyage to the far side of the earth.

And so it happened that these tiny islands became the setting for a strange mystery of the sea.

The ship was the *General Grant*, a sturdy sailer under the command of an experienced captain. She had sailed from Melbourne, Australia, on May 4, 1866, bound for London by way of New Zealand's South Island. On board were passengers, crew, and a cargo of wool, hides, and gold. Exactly how much gold the *General Grant* carried has never been known. But it was a goodly amount—enough to make her whereabouts of great interest later.

The early part of the voyage was uneventful. With good weather, the *General Grant* slipped through mile after mile of ocean. Passengers and crew settled down to shipboard life.

May 13 was a clear, calm day. A light breeze carried the *General Grant* near the Auckland Islands.

Night came and the wind dropped. The ship moved slowly on, carried more by currents than by wind. In midevening a speck of land was sighted: Disappointment Island. The officer on watch checked the ship's position against this landmark. Passengers who had been strolling on deck began to turn in.

A little later the wind died away almost completely. The great sails hung limp, flapping in the uncertain breeze. Rigging rattled as the ocean stirred beneath the hull. A lookout sighted the Auckland Islands, lying dead ahead.

The *General Grant* glided on through the silent night.

An officer, glancing at the land ahead, ordered the course changed by a few points.

The helmsman swung the wheel.

The ship continued on the same course.

Alarmed, the helmsman spun the wheel round and round.

The ship did not respond. She was caught in a current, running strong and sweeping directly toward the rocky islands ahead.

Officers and crew fought to free their ship. They tried by every means at their command to swing her out of the current's grasp.

There was no way they could bring her under control.

A puff of wind would have saved them. But the air hung still, the sails flapped, and the *General Grant* swept on. She came closer and closer to a towering cliff, then crashed into the wall of rock.

Passengers, clad in night clothes, stumbled sleepily onto deck. They found their ship drifting helplessly. She was swinging with the currents, while rocks tore at her bottom and ripped away the rudder. Overhead the cliff loomed out of the darkness.

The *General Grant* backed off, turned slowly in a wide circle, and was caught by still another current. This one drew her toward a different part of the cliff. Here the horrified watchers on the ship saw before them the black mouth of a great cavern.

The *General Grant* was pulled into this vast hole. Wood shrieked against stone. The fore-topmast broke with the crack of a gun. Wood and rigging crashed to the deck. And then the *General Grant* lay still. Passengers and crew heard only a hollow, muffled rumbling—the sound of the sea deep within the cavern.

There was little anyone could do in the pitch black of the cavern's night. The captain ordered the passengers back to their cabins while his men cleared wreckage from the deck.

Dawn came a few hours later. The first gray light of morning showed that the ship lay in a giant cave, hollowed out of the island's rocky heart by the sea. Over hundreds of years, waves and spray and tides had eaten away the rock, wearing it smooth. Nowhere was there a ledge or foothold. The shattered masts of the *General Grant* were jammed against the cavern's roof.

The captain had decided to send off the passengers in the ship's boats and land them on the island. So he first launched three sailors in a small boat that carried gear for hauling the other boats out of the cavern. A second boat also left, carrying the chief officer, three sailors, and a passenger. They were to land on the island and start exploring it.

As the second boat left, the changing tide ground the masts of the *General Grant* against the rocky roof. The main-topmast tore loose and fell in a tangle of rigging and sails. The mainmast was rammed against the roof of the cavern with such force that its bottom tore apart the planking in the hull. The sea rushed in, and the ship began to settle in the water.

Some of the passengers and crew jumped overboard and swam for the cavern's mouth. But May 14 was no calm and quiet day. Wind churned the sea and waves crashed against the rocks. Only four of those in the water escaped to the small boats that were waiting outside.

On board the *General Grant*, some forty passengers and sailors had climbed into the ship's longboat. There was no need to launch the boat. The *General Grant* was sinking so fast that her deck was awash and the longboat afloat. The sailors pulled for the mouth of the cavern. Waves, breaking on the rocks outside, swamped and sank the boat. One passenger, David Ashworth, and two crew members managed to swim out to the boats. The others were lost. Inside the cavern, the *General Grant* went down, carrying with her the captain and most of the passengers and crew.

The survivors in the two small boats waited, listening to the boom of waves inside the cave and watching for signs of life. At last they could wait no longer. The choppy sea threatened to swamp their boats. They turned away, looking for a place to land. The towering cliffs above them offered no shelter for small boats.

Considering winds and tides, they decided to make for Disappointment Island, some ten miles distant. The short voyage took two and a half days because their tiny boats were buffeted by storm-winds and waves. Finally, around noon on May 16, they reached a bay on Disappointment Island and safely beached their boats.

The chief officer, Bartholomew Brown, began to take stock.

He had with him nine seamen and five passengers, one a woman.

The time was mid-May, which is late autumn south of the equator. This meant that an antarctic winter would soon be upon them. It meant, too, that chances of an early rescue were slim. Hunters of whales and seals were not likely to come near the island before spring, if that soon.

The fifteen survivors, then, were likely to spend a number of months on the island.

Brown organized the men to collect driftwood for a fire. The fire warmed them, but that was not its chief purpose. The fire was also their signal, their only hope of attracting the attention of a passing ship. By night its flames would be a beacon. By day wet or green wood thrown on the fire would send up a column of black smoke. At no time could they afford to let the fire go out.

The castaways began to explore the island. One group found a crumbling hut. It became their headquarters and their chief shelter from the winter winds. Another group rowed across to Enderby Island and caught a seal.

Fortunately, seals turned out to be plentiful. Their meat was the castaways' main food. Their skins served as warm clothing and roofing for the hut.

Dreary day followed dreary day, as the survivors of the *General Grant* watched in vain for a passing sail. Slowly the icy winter came to an end.

Spring brought both warmth and hope. The men made rough carvings in the shape of a ship. On each they scratched the name of the *General Grant* and the position of the survivors. They gave each a piece of tin for a sail, hoping that sunlight glinting

on the metal would catch some sailor's eye. They
scratched the same information on pieces of wood,
which they attached to seal bladders. Then they
blew up the bladders and set them adrift.

The currents carried away the messages, but no
help came.

By summer Brown had decided on a desperate
measure. He would take one of the boats and try
to reach the New Zealand coast, about 200 miles
away. He had neither charts nor navigating instruments, but the weather was fair and he felt his
chances of making land were good.

The men decked over a boat with sealskins and
made a sail out of some old canvas. They provisioned
the boat with water, smoked seal meat, the eggs of
sea birds, and tins of soup that had come with them
from the *General Grant*.

On January 22, 1867, Brown and three sailors
launched their small boat and set out for New Zealand. They were never heard from again.

Autumn came, then winter. And still no ship had
passed close enough to see the signal.

In September one of the crew members became
sick and died.

On October 6, the ten survivors saw a ship sailing eastward. Surely she was close enough to see
their fire! They piled wet wood on it and sent up a

A ship passed without seeing their signal

thick column of smoke. The ship sailed on out of sight.

The castaways had now been on Disappointment Island for nearly eighteen months. Despairing of rescue there, they decided to move to Enderby, which was a little closer to the shipping routes.

They were closer but still, apparently, not close enough. On November 19, a ship passed without seeing their signal.

Two days later another ship appeared on the horizon. This time the castaways did not bother with the fire. They launched their boat and rowed toward that distant sail with all the strength they possessed. The ship, the whaler *Amherst*, saw them, stopped, and took them aboard.

With the rescue of the survivors, the story of the *General Grant* and her sunken gold spread through New Zealand. Since everyone knew where the ship had gone down, expeditions were organized to hunt for the wreckage and treasure. One of them was led by David Ashworth, former passenger on the *General Grant*.

He set sail aboard the schooner *Daphne* on March 26, 1870. The ship reached the Aucklands without difficulty. There, on a fair, calm day, Ashworth, the captain, and four of the crew set off in one of the *Daphne's* boats.

They never came back.

Weeks later the three remaining crew members brought the *Daphne* back to her home port on South Island. They had waited and waited for the boat until all hope was gone. Then they had set sail and left the Aucklands.

What happened to the men from the *Daphne*? Was their boat wrecked on rocks? Was it drawn into some deep crevice of the cavern from which there was no escape? Was Ashworth, who had once escaped the cavern, claimed by it the second time?

No one has ever known. Nor did anyone ever find the *General Grant*. Though the searchers knew exactly where to hunt, they found no trace of the ship or gold. The dark cavern in the heart of the rocky island guards its secrets to this day.

The Nag's Head Portrait

IN THE summer of 1869, Dr. William G. Pool of
Elizabeth City, North Carolina, took his family to
the seashore for a few weeks. The place he chose
was a small resort called Nag's Head. It lay on one
of the long sandbank islands separating the ocean
from the coast of the Carolinas.

The islands, or banks, had a strange and cruel
history. In the past, many ships had been wrecked on
them. And the inhabitants of the sandbanks, a brutal
group of people known as "bankers," lived by pirat-
ing the wrecks. They murdered the passengers and
crews, then plundered the ships. When the sea did
not provide them with wrecks, the "bankers" created
them by luring passing ships onto the shoals.

Nag's Head had won its name through just such
a vicious practice. On stormy nights the "bankers"
would hobble a horse, tie a lantern around its neck,

and walk it up and down the beach. Sailors at sea mistook the bobbing light for that of a ship riding safely at anchor. They steered for shelter, only to be wrecked on the banks and killed so that they could tell no tales.

By 1869, however, lighthouses and law had put an end to the wrecking and plundering of ships. Nag's Head had become a small resort town. And the "bankers" were simply year-round inhabitants who gathered what the sea washed up on the beaches. Only the older people remembered the days of piracy.

One of these was a sick woman, a Mrs. Mann, to whose bedside Dr. Pool was called.

Arriving at her home, the doctor found a crude hut built of timbers from old wrecks and thatched with reeds. The inside was dark, dirty, and cluttered. But in the dusty disorder one object stood out: the portrait of a beautiful young woman.

Painted on a wooden panel, the portrait showed a woman in her middle or late twenties. She had piercing black eyes and black hair tinged with reddish-brown. Her skin was fair, her cheeks pink. She wore a white dress cut square at the neck, a fashion popular in the early 1800's.

From the moment he saw it, the portrait fascinated Dr. Pool. Who was this young woman? How had her portrait come to a "banker's" hut at Nag's Head? An exciting possibility sprang to mind, but at first he could learn nothing about the portrait from his patient. Mrs. Mann was sullen by nature and suspicious of outsiders. She had called in the doctor only because she was suffering from an illness that no home remedy had been able to cure.

However, as time passed and she grew better under his treatment, Mrs. Mann came to trust the doctor. And, when she was cured, she gave him the portrait in payment for his services. She was still reluctant to talk about the painting. But before the summer ended, Dr. Pool managed to draw from her an account of how the portrait came to Nag's Head. Her story confirmed the idea that had been growing in his mind. He now felt sure that the portrait was a major clue to a mystery that had gone unsolved for fifty-six years: the loss of the schooner *Patriot*, which carried as a passenger one of the country's outstanding women, Theodosia Burr Alston.

In December, 1812, the *Patriot* was refitting at Georgetown, South Carolina. Her guns were dismounted and hidden below deck. Her name was painted out. Every sign of her recent activity was completely erased.

Built originally as a pilot boat, the *Patriot* had

been acting as a privateer during the War of 1812—commissioned by the United States Government to prey on British merchant shipping. Fast, sturdy, and well-sailed, the *Patriot* had captured a rich haul of spoils. Now her master, Captain Overstocks, wanted to make a quick run to New York with his cargo. On the way he would have to pass a fleet of British naval ships. So it was essential that the *Patriot*'s privateering past be hidden.

By late December the job was done and the *Patriot* ready. On sailing day three passengers came aboard. One was Theodosia, daughter of Aaron Burr and wife of Joseph Alston, governor of South Carolina.

Then twenty-nine years old, she was famed for her beauty, charm, and intelligence. But at this time she was ill, listless, and heartsick. Her health had been poor all through her marriage, for the hot, wet climate of her husband's rice plantation did not agree with her. In June, 1812, her only child, a boy of ten, had died of a fever that was probably malaria. His death was a blow from which she had not recovered and for which she could find no comfort.

Theodosia's husband and father were gravely concerned about her. They decided that she should go north for a visit with Burr, who had recently returned from four years in Europe. Perhaps a change of climate and a reunion with the father she adored would restore her health and spirits.

Alston could not accompany his wife. As governor, he was forbidden by state law to leave South Carolina during his term of office. Burr, therefore, had sent Timothy Green, an old friend who had some medical knowledge, south to travel with Theodosia. Green and Alston agreed that a land journey by horse-drawn coach would be too much of a strain on Theodosia. So Green booked passage for Theodosia, her maid, and himself on the *Patriot*, the fastest ship available. In case of trouble, Alston gave Captain Overstocks a letter to the admiral of the British fleet. In it he asked that the ship carrying his sick wife be allowed to proceed without delay to New York.

At noon on Thursday, December 30, the *Patriot* sailed with the tide from Georgetown on what should have been a swift five- or six-day voyage to New York.

The days passed and became weeks. In New York, Burr paced the water front, watching for a sail that never appeared. In South Carolina, Alston waited for a letter that never came. At last it became clear that the *Patriot* could not be overdue. Somewhere, somehow, between Georgetown and New York, she had been lost.

There were no clues to what had happened. But it seemed probable that the *Patriot* had met her end in one of three ways, for she had sailed into waters that held three known dangers: winter storms, an enemy fleet, and the pirate ships that then infested the waters off the Southern states.

For a time Burr hoped that the ship had been captured by the British or by pirates and Theodosia taken prisoner. Then, as the months crept by without news, the conviction grew in his heart that Theodosia was dead. Like Alston, he came to believe that the *Patriot* had sunk in a storm with all aboard.

There was, of course, no proof that a storm had sunk the *Patriot*. And so, perhaps it is not strange that another story began to circulate. Rumor said that the *Patriot* had really been captured and scuttled by pirates. According to this story, while the *Patriot* was refitting at Georgetown, her crew gossiped about the rich cargo their ship carried. Alerted by the gossip and knowing that the *Patriot* was unarmed, pirates lay in wait for her. Under armed attack, the *Patriot* surrendered. The pirates then killed all aboard, plundered the ship, and sank her.

At the time of the *Patriot*'s loss, there was no evidence whatsoever to support the pirate theory. But, starting some twenty years later, evidence of a kind began to turn up. It took the form of deathbed confessions made by sick and aged pirates.

The first such confession was made in the early 1830's by a former pirate who was dying in Mobile, Alabama. An account printed in the *Alabama Journal* reads:

". . . It appears from the statement of a respectable merchant of Mobile that a man died in that city recently, who confessed on his dying bed that he had been a pirate and helped to destroy the vessel and all the crew and passengers, on which Mrs. Alston had embarked for New York. He declared, says this gentleman (who is well known to us), that after the men were all killed there was an unwillingness on the part of every pirate to take the life of Mrs. Alston, who had not resisted them or fought them, and therefore they drew lots who should perform the deed, as it had to be done.

"The lot fell on this pirate who declares that he effected his object by laying a plank along the edge of the ship and made Mrs. Alston walk on the plank till it tilted over with her. The dying pirate (says our informant) requested his physician to make this story public; but his surviving family will not permit that the name of the deceased should be known."

Other confessions followed. Two criminals about to be executed in Norfolk, Virginia, admitted that they had been among the crew who boarded the *Patriot* and forced Theodosia to walk the plank. A sailor dying in Texas made a similar confession.

A detailed confession was published in a book, *Fernando de Lemos*, that was described by the author as being both truth and fiction. Chapter XXIX was headed "The Fate of the Daughter of Aaron Burr Revealed." In this chapter, a Dr. Rhineberg was called to attend a sick old pirate named Dominique You. Learning that he had only a short time to live, the pirate told the story of his life to the doctor. Near the end of his account, You said: "On the 3rd of January, 1813, there occurred an event . . . which I have ever since bitterly regretted. . . . We were in the latitude of Cape Hatteras on the coast of North Carolina, when we met a small schooner named the *Patriot,* which had been dismantled by a late storm, and which was bound from Charleston, South Carolina, to New York. She was a vessel famous for her sailing qualities. After many successful privateering cruises against the English, she was going home loaded with rich spoils, and with her guns stowed below—which circumstances made her incapable of defense. We boarded her. She was commanded by an experienced captain, and had for a sailing-master an old New York pilot noted for his skill and courage.

"Such men could not be allowed to live to tell
tales, and perhaps avenge their mishap at our hands,
even if sparing them had not been contrary to the
regulations of our association. They were slaughtered and thrown overboard with the rest of the
crew. After this execution my men rushed down
below and brought up to the deck a woman of sur-
passing beauty, deadly pale, but showing no other
sign of terror. . . . 'Who are you?' I said to her.
'Theodosia Burr, the daughter of Aaron Burr, ex-
vice-president of the United States, and wife of
Joseph Alston, governor of South Carolina.' "

An argument took place among the pirates as to
what they were going to do with Theodosia. Finally,
You put an end to the matter by saying, "Death to
prisoners is a necessity of the war we wage. Every
vessel we take is to be scuttled and every soul on
board must perish. . . ." Then, his account goes on,
"I had the plank laid out. She stepped on it and de-
scended into the sea with graceful composure, as
if she had been alighting from a carriage. She sank,
and rising again, she, with an indescribable smile
of angelic sweetness, waved her hand . . . and then
sank forever."

Such accounts were seized on by many people as
proof that the *Patriot* had met her end in the hands
of pirates. Yet the confessions really cannot be ac-

cepted as evidence. There is no way of proving them true, and there is good reason to question them.

The Dominique You story, with its wealth of detail, is particularly tempting. But the author himself described his book as being both truth and fiction. And it seems likely that You's confession is just that. The known facts about the *Patriot* were the truth; You himself, so far as is known, was fiction.

The other confessions also raise some very large questions. How much reliance can be placed on the word of a criminal? How much reliance can be placed on the word of those faced with death after a lifetime of evil-doing? Fear-stricken, they repented. Repenting, they drew the sympathy of the good and kind people who visited them. To hold this sympathy and attention, some may have confessed to crimes they had not committed. And the most attention-catching crime would certainly have been the plundering of the *Patriot*.

One other incident also throws doubt on the pirate confessions. This was the chance meeting of an American general, Thomas Pinckney, with the admiral of the British fleet stationed off the Carolinas in the winter of 1812–1813. They met at a dinner party in London, years after the loss of the *Patriot*. The admiral stated that he had seen the ship carrying Mrs. Alston, had received and read Governor

Alston's letter, and had granted the ship permission to proceed. He added, however, that a terrible storm had struck that same night, January 1. It was violent enough to scatter the fleet, and the admiral believed that the storm must have sunk the *Patriot*.

The admiral, of course, had not seen the *Patriot* go down. That part of his statement is belief, not proof. But his statement does establish two facts. First, on January 1 the *Patriot* was safe; she had not been attacked by pirates or British warships. Second, she ran into a bad winter storm on the night of January 1, a storm which had scattered the fleet.

The *Patriot* may or may not have sunk in that storm. She may or may not have been disabled in it. But the storm and the presence of the British fleet make it most unlikely that she was attacked by pirates. They could not have attacked and boarded her in such a storm—far less have made anyone walk the plank. And they would not have attacked in waters held by British naval ships. The risk of being attacked by the British was too great.

So it was known only that the *Patriot* had been in a storm. Somehow, during or after the storm, she was lost. That was how matters stood when Dr. Pool discovered the Nag's Head portrait in 1869. The portrait and the story told by Mrs. Mann opened up still another possibility.

Mrs. Mann explained that she had been twice married and twice widowed. Her first husband was a young fisherman and "banker" named Joseph Tillett, whom she had married when she was about sixteen. During their courtship, Tillett had given her several presents: the portrait; a vase of wax flowers under a glass globe; a beautifully carved shell; two black silk dresses made for a gentlewoman of small build; and a lace head covering.

These gifts had come from a disabled ship that Tillett and the other "bankers" had spied being driven in toward the banks. They boarded the ship and found her deserted, except for a small black-and-tan dog. They saw no blood or other signs of violence, but the disorder of the cabins indicated that the ship had been ransacked.

The "bankers" found nothing that told them the name of the ship, her home port, or her destination. Nor, Tillett claimed, could they find much of value. There were some silks and silver but little else of worth. The men divided what they had found. As his share, Tillett took the portrait, which was hanging on the wall of a cabin that had clearly been occupied by a woman. From this cabin he also took the dresses and other items that he later gave to the girl he was courting.

The "bankers," Mrs. Mann said, believed that

the ship had been captured and plundered at sea by
pirates. For reasons the "bankers" could not guess,
the pirates had failed to scuttle or burn the ship.

Mrs. Mann could not remember the date of this
shipwreck. But, questioned closely by the doctor,
she did remember that it happened in the winter
when "we were fighting the English on the sea."
Since in 1869 Mrs. Mann was about seventy years
old, she could not be talking about the Revolution-
ary War. She must, the doctor decided, mean the
War of 1812 and the winter of 1812–1813.

This was all the information Dr. Pool could get
from Mrs. Mann, though he always suspected that
she knew more than she had told him. But it was
enough to convince him that the wrecked ship
could well have been the *Patriot* and the woman in
the portrait Theodosia. For many of the facts in
Mrs. Mann's story tallied with those known about
the *Patriot*.

The date was right. The ship had been driven
toward Nag's Head at the time the *Patriot* was lost.

The place was right. The *Patriot* was last seen off
Cape Hatteras.

The kind of ship was right. The wrecked ship was
described by Mrs. Mann as a pilot-boat-built
schooner—just what the *Patriot* was. And, like the
Patriot, the wrecked ship was nameless.

In addition, the portrait resembled Theodosia in eyes, hair, coloring, and features. The two dresses, which Mrs. Mann still had, were right for a woman of Theodosia's build and social position.

On the whole, there seemed to be a strong possibility that the ship wrecked near Nag's Head had been the *Patriot*. And the possibility was further strengthened by another story that came to light when Dr. Pool's discovery was made public.

A distant relative of the Burr family, a Mrs. Drake, visited the Pools to see the Nag's Head portrait. And she told them what had until then been a family story concerning still another deathbed confession.

The pirate in this case was an old man named Benjamin Franklin Burdick. In his last years, the story of the *Patriot* was apparently much on Burdick's mind. He told it over and over, weeping as he did so, to the family with whom he lived in Michigan. In 1850 he was moved to the Cass County Poorhouse in Cassopolis, Michigan. There he told it again to a poorhouse visitor, a Mrs. Parks, wife of a Methodist minister, who in turn told it to Mrs. Drake's grandmother.

Repenting of a life filled with wrong-doing and crime, Burdick told Mrs. Parks that the act which caused him the greatest sorrow was the tipping of the plank on which Mrs. Alston walked into the sea. Describing the episode, Burdick said, "I was a sailor on a pirate vessel. We captured the vessel in which the lady was. When told she must walk the plank into the ocean, she asked for a few minutes alone, which was granted. She came forward when told her time had expired, dressed beautifully in white, the loveliest woman I had ever seen. Calmly she stepped upon the plank. With eyes raised to the heavens and hands crossed reverently upon her bosom, she walked slowly and firmly into the ocean, without an apparent tremor. . . ."

From time to time, as he retold the story, Burdick added other details. The date had been January, 1813. Mrs. Alston had worn a blue ribbon at her throat. She had knelt and prayed for all the pirates, her loved ones, and herself. She had asked that word be sent to her husband and father so that they would not always be expecting her. She had told them that her only child was dead. According to some accounts, Burdick also said that there had been a little black-and-tan dog aboard the ship and a portrait hanging on a cabin wall.

Burdick's story, of course, is open to the same criticism as the other pirate confessions. He was a criminal. And he was old, sick, and fearful of dying.

Yet two things about his confession make it worth considering.

The first is that it has a ring of eyewitness truth. An uneducated man, Burdick could not have read up on the *Patriot*. Of low mentality, he lacked the imagination to invent details like the blue ribbon or the request to send word to Alston and Burr.

The second is that his story fits perfectly with Mrs. Mann's. They appeared to be talking about the same ship. And the same false note occurs in both stories. Both claimed that the piracy took place on the high seas.

Mrs. Mann stated that the ship had been plundered at sea before the "bankers" boarded her. But sea pirates would not have left silk and silver aboard the ship. Nor would they have left the vessel afloat as a silent witness to their crime.

Burdick described himself as a sea pirate. But the storm and the British fleet made it almost impossible for sea pirates to have attacked the *Patriot*.

All this suggests that Mrs. Mann and Burdick may have lied about the same thing for the same reason. It is wholly possible that the men who plundered the *Patriot* and murdered all aboard were not sea pirates but land pirates. It is possible that the *Patriot* was disabled by the storm of January 1, 1813, and driven, helpless, toward Nag's Head. The "bankers"—Tillett and Burdick among them—swarmed out to meet the ship. They slaughtered the men and forced Theodosia to walk the plank. The little dog, then, was not the only living creature aboard when the "bankers" found the ship, but the only creature left alive when they finished their bloody deed.

Burdick may have lied to protect men still living at Nag's Head in 1850. Mrs. Mann may also have lied—or perhaps Tillett did not tell her the full story of what had happened.

The land pirate theory makes more sense than any other. Yet even in 1869 no one could prove it true or false.

Burdick was dead. There was no way of finding out whether he had indeed been a land pirate.

Mrs. Mann had told all she was willing or able to.

No trace remained of the ship that might—or might not—have been the *Patriot*.

There was only the portrait. Was it or was it not of Theodosia?

By 1869 all the people who had known Theodosia were dead. No one could look at the portrait and say, "Yes, that is how she looked in 1812," or "No, that is not Theodosia." The painting could only be compared with other portraits of her. And the comparison proved nothing. The earlier portraits of a

The Nag's Head portrait (left) and a portrait of
Theodosia (right)

younger Theodosia were done by the leading paint-
ers of the day. The Nag's Head portrait is the work
of a less talented artist painting an older woman.
It could be Theodosia—or simply someone who resembled her. The painting itself yields no clue. It
is not signed.

Nor did any written record of the portrait turn
up. It is not mentioned in the letters that passed
between Burr and Alston. No record of it was found
in the Alston family papers—though such a record
might well have been destroyed during the Civil
War.

A number of people who have studied the portraits of Theodosia believe that she is the woman in
the Nag's Head portrait. They suggest that she had
the portrait painted as a present for her father. This
may well be so. But then it is strange that someone
took the painting out of its wrappings and hung it
in Theodosia's cabin for a voyage of only five or six
days.

On the other hand, it is possible that the ship was
the *Patriot* but that the portrait was not of Theodosia. It could, say, have been the captain's wife. It
could have been a portrait taken from one of the
British ships that the *Patriot* looted.

Or perhaps the ship was not the *Patriot* at all.
Perhaps the *Patriot* went down with merciful quick-

ness in a storm, as Burr, Alston, and the admiral believed.

Whatever the truth may be, there is only one clue: the unknown woman in the Nag's Head portrait.

Inquiry on the *Waratah*

On APRIL 27, 1909, the steamer *Waratah* left London for Australia, by way of South Africa's Cape of Good Hope. Designed for this run, she had already made one successful round trip in generally fair weather.

The outward half of her second trip was also made in good weather. The ship reached Australia without incident, took on a new cargo, and set out for home.

Her first port of call on the homeward passage was Durban, South Africa, where she unloaded some 240 tons of cargo. The *Waratah* left Durban at 8:15 on the evening of July 26, heading for Cape Town and then London. Aboard were 92 passengers and a crew of 119.

About six o'clock the next morning the *Waratah* was sighted by the *Clan MacIntyre*, a smaller, slower steamer that was following the same route. The two ships exchanged signals.

CLAN MACINTYRE: What ship?

WARATAH: *Waratah* for London.

CLAN MACINTYRE: *Clan MacIntyre* for London. What weather did you have from Australia?

WARATAH: Strong southwesterly to southerly winds, across.

CLAN MACINTYRE: Thanks. Good-by. Pleasant passage.

WARATAH: Thanks. Same to you. Good-by.

The *Waratah* then overhauled the smaller steamer and pulled ahead. A few hours later she was simply a dot on the horizon. The last trace of her smoke soon vanished. So far as is known, no one ever saw the *Waratah* again.

July 29, the day she was due in Cape Town, came and went. At first no one worried. The *Clan MacIntyre* and other ships had encountered heavy seas and gale winds on July 27. On July 28, they had beaten their way through hurricane winds in one of the worst storms any of their captains remembered. So it seemed likely that the *Waratah* had simply been delayed. Smaller, older ships had all come safely through the storms.

More days passed. The *Waratah* was now considerably overdue at Cape Town. Ships that had left

Durban after the *Waratah* began to arrive. They could give no news of her. They had sighted neither the ship nor any wreckage, though they had followed the same route.

It hardly seemed possible that the *Waratah* could have sunk without a trace. The ship was new, less than a year old. She had powerful, coal-burning engines that could push her along at a speed of thirteen knots. Her captain, J. E. Ilbery, was a veteran sailor who had been at sea nearly all his life. And the *Waratah* carried a generous supply of life-

saving equipment—boats, rafts, life belts, flares, signals, and lights. It was true that she had no radio equipment, but neither did most ocean-going ships of that period. The *Waratah* was as up to date as any ship afloat.

No, it seemed much more likely that she had had a mechanical breakdown of some sort. Perhaps she had lost a propeller and was drifting helplessly. Similar accidents had happened to other ships. Only ten years before, a fine ship named the *Waikato* had broken down and drifted for fourteen weeks before being towed into port. So a search was organized for the *Waratah*.

The area between Durban and Cape Town was thoroughly searched, but no trace of the ship was found. The search was broadened. Ships hunted for her as far away as the Crozets and St. Paul Island.

All ships in the general area were asked to keep a
lookout for the *Waratah*, her boats, or survivors.

But the weeks and months passed without news
of the missing ship. At length it became certain that
the *Waratah* could no longer be afloat. She would
have to be added to the long list of ships lost without a trace.

When a ship is lost at sea, an official inquiry is
held. Its purpose is to discover what happened; to
fix blame, if there is blame to be fixed; and, if possible, to prevent a similar accident from happening.

The inquiry on the loss of the *Waratah* was held
at Westminster, in London. It began in December,
1910, and continued into February, 1911.

The most important evidence came from the
captain of the *Clan MacIntyre*. He told of sighting
the *Waratah* early in the morning of July 27. And he
told of the weather that his ship—and presumably
the *Waratah*—had steamed into. "We experienced
a great storm—I had never met with anything so
bad on this coast during my thirteen years in the
trade," the captain said. "The wind seemed to tear
the water up and was of quite exceptional fierceness
and power, rising at times fully to hurricane force.
There was a tremendous sea." At times his ship had
been forced backward by winds and waves, but the
Clan MacIntyre came safely through.

Her captain also reported that during July 27 and 28 he had sighted ten other ships. But he had not again seen the *Waratah* after she overhauled his ship.

Nor had any of those ten ships seen the *Waratah*.

Other captains added what little they knew. But their evidence tended to deepen the mystery rather than explain what had happened to the *Waratah*.

At 9:30 in the evening of July 27, the steamer *Guelph* had sighted a large passenger ship not far from the South African port of East London. Using signal lanterns, the *Guelph* flashed her name to the other ship. The other ship replied, but her signal was so faint that the *Guelph*'s third officer could make out only the last three letters. These were TAH.

The ship, then, could—or could not—have been the *Waratah*. If she was, then the *Waratah* must have broken down, for she was sighted only seventy miles from where the *Clan MacIntyre* had seen her at six o'clock in the morning. A breakdown was certainly possible. But then it was strange that the *Waratah* had not been overtaken by the *Clan MacIntyre*, plodding steadily along behind her.

Evidence from the *Harlow* added even more confusion. The *Harlow* was steaming along the coast of South Africa in late afternoon that same day. About six o'clock, the captain noticed the smoke of another steamer, about twenty or twenty-five miles away. There was so much smoke that he wondered if the ship could be on fire.

The evening darkened. In line with where he had seen the smoke, the *Harlow*'s captain now noted a ship's lights—two masthead lights and a light at the stern.

A couple of hours later he again saw the lights. He judged that they belonged to a fast steamer coming up behind him.

The captain went into the charthouse for a few minutes. When he returned to the bridge, he saw two bright flashes arc through the night sky. He thought they were caused by an explosion. But the *Harlow*'s mate thought they were simply bush fires on shore. Whatever the case, the lights of the steamer they had seen were gone.

When the captain later heard of the *Waratah*'s disappearance, he began to wonder whether this was the ship he had seen. Had she been on fire and perhaps blown up?

On the whole, this was unlikely. For one thing, the *Harlow* was heading *toward* Durban and so, of course, was the ship behind her. The *Waratah* was traveling *away* from Durban. Then, too, if the *Waratah* had been on fire, she had plenty of time to get her boats away, for the weather was not yet really bad. Finally, no one heard an explosion; and no one saw distress flares.

Probably the lights sighted by the *Harlow* were those of some ship other than the *Waratah*. The bright flashes were most likely bush fires, as the mate thought. Bush fires were common along the coast in July.

From two other ships came reports of having sighted bodies in the sea.

The third officer of the *Tottenham* told the court of inquiry that on August 11 he had seen what looked like bodies floating in the water between East London and the mouth of the Bashee River. A young crew member and the second mate described one of the bodies as that of a girl dressed in red.

The *Tottenham*'s captain and chief engineer, however, said that the objects were not human bodies. For the most part they were fish and pieces of blubber. "The girl in red" was actually a big roll of printing paper with a red wrapper.

The captain of the steamer *Insizwa* also reported having seen bodies on August 11. But the *Insizwa* was about 100 miles away from the *Tottenham* at the time. So the bodies or objects seen were not the same. And again there was disagreement aboard ship as to what had been seen. Several of the

Insizwa's officers were sure that the objects in the
sea were not human bodies.

The court did not accept either report of sighting
bodies.

Only the evidence of the *Clan MacIntyre* could
be accepted as reliable. The *Waratah* had last been
seen on the morning of July 27. She was then following a course that must have taken her into a terrible storm.

What could have happened to the *Waratah* in
this storm? That was the chief question before the
court. And most of the evidence had to do with
whether or not the *Waratah* was a stable ship.

Well before the inquiry opened, rumors had been
going around about this. Seagoing friends of Captain Ilbery claimed that he was unhappy about the
way the *Waratah* handled. She was top-heavy.
When she rolled in a heavy sea, she was a long time
coming back to an upright position. The same com-
plaints, others said, had been made by officers who
had sailed on the *Waratah*—and gone down with
her.

The owners, of course, denied these rumors. The
Waratah, they declared, was a stable, seaworthy,
well-designed ship. They called a series of expert
witnesses who backed up this view. The owners
pointed out that the *Waratah* had passed five in-

spections after she was built. She had been given the highest rating in each.

There was just one weak point in the owners' case. They could not, or would not, produce Captain Ilbery's report on how the ship handled.

The captain of a new ship always reports to the owners on her. With the *Waratah* such a report would have been extremely important. The owners were thinking of using the same design for a second ship. Naturally, they would be eager for the captain's opinion. But the letters and reports that they offered the court contained no hint of what Captain Ilbery had thought.

The court found this suspicious.

It then heard evidence from former passengers on the *Waratah* and from crew members who had left the ship. Here it was hard to tell what was truth and what was fancy.

Some crewmen from the *Waratah*'s first voyage had found the ship's behavior completely normal. Others had found it no such thing.

The fourth engineer reported, "She neither pitched nor rolled nor anything out of the ordinary." A former deck officer agreed with him.

But coal trimmer William Marshall said that the *Waratah*'s rolling had made him uneasy. He wanted to leave the ship, and did. An experienced able-bodied seaman told the court, "She was the un-steadiest ship I ever voyaged in." Another seaman stated that when he was signing on the ship the chief officer told him, "If you can get anything else, take it. This ship will be a coffin for somebody." The seaman took the advice and left the ship in Australia. Other seamen described the *Waratah* as "dead on the roll." They meant that when she rolled with the sea, she stayed over longer than a good ship should. The ship's surgeon from the first voyage agreed. He told of a sudden jerk that had rolled him out of his bath one morning. He, too, had decided to leave the *Waratah*.

The former passengers were also divided in opinion.

"I have made three voyages to Australia round the Cape of Good Hope," Mr. Worthington Church said. "I thought the *Waratah* was very top-heavy. I had a conversation with Captain Ilbery, who said he was not altogether satisfied with the ship." Other passengers agreed with Mr. Church, testifying that the *Waratah* had rolled a great deal.

But Mr. Morley Johnson had sailed on the same trip as Mr. Church. He told the court that the *Waratah*'s behavior was equal to that of any ship he had ever been in. "Her rolling was not unusual," he said. "No person ever expressed to me any doubt of the ship's stability." A number of other passengers agreed with Mr. Johnson.

One who disagreed, though, was William Bragg, professor of physics at the University of Leeds and an expert on motion. The rolling of the *Waratah* had alarmed Professor Bragg. He felt that she tended to roll over and stay over. He believed that she lacked sufficient righting moment—the force that brings a stable ship back to the upright from a roll.

Then, too, there was the evidence of Mr. Claude G. Sawyer. He was one of the very few survivors who had sailed from Sydney, Australia, on that last voyage.

The first part of the trip had made him extremely uneasy. He thought the *Waratah* rolled too much and too far. One morning, studying the level of water in his bath, he concluded that the ship was lying over at a 45-degree angle. Sometimes, he said, she recovered from a roll with such a violent jerk that passengers were thrown about and injured.

Alarmed, Mr. Sawyer spoke to one of the officers. The officer assured him that nothing was wrong with the ship. Then he spoke to another passenger, a Mr. Ebsworth, who had once been a sailor. Mr. Ebsworth was also worried. "The rolling," he said, "is not all. Go and look at how she is pitching." They

watched the bow of the ship in the water. The bow
rose and slid over one wave. But then, instead of
rising to the next wave, the ship stayed down and
plowed through it.

Thoroughly alarmed now, Mr. Sawyer began to
think of leaving the ship at Durban. But the voyage
continued calmly enough. Nothing happened, and
Mr. Sawyer thought he would stay aboard after
all.

Then, three or four days out of Durban, all his
fears returned because of a terrible dream. In this
dream he was called for by a man wearing blood-
stained armor and holding a long sword in his right
hand. Three times Mr. Sawyer dreamed this dream.
Convinced that the dream was a warning, he left
the *Waratah* at Durban and booked passage on another ship. He cabled to his wife: "Thought
Waratah top-heavy. Landed Durban."

On July 28, before anyone knew that the *Waratah*
was missing, Mr. Sawyer had another dream. This
time he saw the ship plowing through a heavy sea.
A great wave broke over her bow. The *Waratah*
rolled over onto her side and sank.

Mr. Sawyer's dreams proved only that he had
been deeply worried by the *Waratah*. But his worry
could not be brushed aside. He was an experienced
traveler, making his thirteenth long ocean voyage.

And many others from the *Waratah* had shared that same worry.

On February 22, 1911, the court of inquiry reported its findings. The court found "that the ship was lost in the gale of the 28th of July, 1909, which was of exceptional violence for those waters and was the first great storm she had encountered. The court is led to this conclusion by the fact that she overhauled the *Clan MacIntyre* which afterwards experienced the gale, was last seen heading in a direction which would take her into a position where she would feel the full force of the storm, and was never afterwards sighted by the *Clan MacIntyre*. Had she been only disabled it is almost certain that she would have been so sighted. . . ."

The court could not say definitely how the *Waratah* was lost. But it believed that she had capsized.

It seemed the only possible explanation. The *Waratah*, caught in the terrible storm, must have rolled far over, hung there for a dreadful moment, and then gone all the way over and down.

Yet no one will ever know for sure why or where the big, new steamer *Waratah* vanished from the sight of men.

The Mystery of the *Mary Celeste*

WITH a brisk northerly wind filling her sails, the
Dei Gratia was knifing through the swells of the
Atlantic that fourth day of December, 1872. At the
time, she was some twenty days out of New York,
carrying a cargo of petroleum, and heading for
Gibraltar. Aboard were her captain, David Reed
Morehouse, and a crew of seven.

In the early afternoon, Captain Morehouse
checked the ship's position and found that they
were about 600 miles from Portugal. A short time
later he sighted another ship, several miles ahead.
At first she was just a smudge on the horizon. But,
since she was sailing toward the *Dei Gratia*, Morehouse soon got a better look at her.

The stranger was carrying very little sail. And,
as Morehouse noted, her sails were trimmed wrong
for the northerly wind. Also, the ship was being

Morehouse hailed her again and again

badly handled—so badly that he wondered if there was anyone at the wheel.

As the *Dei Gratia* neared the other ship, Morehouse hailed her through his speaking trumpet. He hailed her again and again. Silence was the only reply.

This was odd indeed. Morehouse decided to investigate. Ordering a boat lowered, he sent Oliver Deveau, his first mate, and two seamen over to see what was wrong.

The men rowed their boat under the stern of the stranger and saw her name—*Mary Celeste.* Deveau and a seaman climbed aboard. They found themselves on what appeared to be a deserted ship. There was no one to be seen. There was nothing to be heard but the sound of the wind in the rigging and the slap of water against the hull.

Deveau immediately checked the pumps to make sure the ship was not sinking. There was, he found, three and a half feet of water in the hold. This was not a dangerous amount. And, since the pumps were in good working condition, the water could easily be forced out.

He then began to explore the silent ship.

In the captain's cabin the berth had been slept in but not made up. The bedding had been dented by the body of a small child. Deveau found the cap-ain's clothes, as well as those of a woman and a child. He found a doll and other toys. He noted that clothes, books, furniture, and charts were all in good order. So was the rosewood melodeon, a musical instrument something like a small organ. His search turned up a small amount of money and some jewelry, including a gold locket. Under the captain's berth Deveau found an old sword, its blade covered with what seemed to be rust.

He went forward to the crew's quarters. Again he saw no one. Again everything was in order, the seamen's chests neatly stowed. It was as if the men had stepped away for a few minutes. They had left behind their pipes, razors, money, oilskins, and boots. Laundry hung from the drying line.

In the galley, pots, pans, and dishes were clean. There was no cooked food lying around here, or anywhere else on the ship. The galley and store-rooms held a six-month supply of meat, potatoes, flour, and other food. The ship's casks contained a plentiful supply of water.

Deveau finished his inspection and went back to the *Dei Gratia*. He was fully satisfied that there was no one aboard the *Mary Celeste*. But neither were there many clues as to what had happened aboard her.

As he told Captain Morehouse, the *Mary Celeste*

had clearly been abandoned. Her boat was gone.
So were the ship's papers and the navigating instruments. It was equally clear that she had been abandoned hastily. There had been no time to collect
money, jewelry, or other valuables.

Deveau thought she had probably been abandoned in the morning of November 25. The last
entry in the logbook was for November 24. It
showed the *Mary Celeste* as being about 110 miles
west of the island of Santa Maria in the Azores.
There was an entry on the log slate for 8 A.M.,
November 25. The *Mary Celeste* was then six miles
off the eastern point of Santa Maria. That was the
last record of any kind, and it gave no hint of
trouble or danger.

At eight o'clock on the morning of November 25
all had been normal. Breakfast had been already
served and eaten, the dishes and pans washed up.
The ship's position had been recorded on the log
slate. And then?

Deveau had no idea. The ship struck him as being
perfectly seaworthy. He had seen no sign of fire,
explosion, or collision. The cargo—barrels of alcohol
—was in good condition and well stowed. Deveau
had noticed just one curious thing. The cargo hatch
—the sliding wooden cover over the hold—was off
and lying on the deck. So were two other hatches.

But this did not necessarily mean anything. The only certain facts were that the ship had been abandoned about ten days earlier and had sailed on by herself until the meeting with the *Dei Gratia*.

Morehouse and Deveau discussed what to do next. If they could bring the *Mary Celeste* into port, they could enter a claim for salvage. The claim should bring them a good sum of money because both the ship and her cargo were valuable. The question was: Could they get her into port?

They decided to try. Deveau and two of the men went back aboard the *Mary Celeste*. Morehouse sailed off in the *Dei Gratia*.

Deveau brought the *Mary Celeste* into Gibraltar on the morning of December 13, only twelve hours after the *Dei Gratia* had arrived. Morehouse immediately filed a claim for salvage. Cables were sent to New York. And the Vice-Admiralty Court in Gibraltar began hearings on the salvage claim.

At this time, no one was very concerned about the *Mary Celeste's* people. Everyone felt sure their boat had been picked up by a passing ship and that they would soon be heard from. Attention was focused on the *Mary Celeste* herself.

She was, it seemed, a Nova Scotia-built ship, eleven years old, and a sturdy carrier of cargo. She had changed hands several times, and at the period of this last voyage was owned by several men. The two main owners were Captain James H. Winchester of New York and Captain Benjamin S. Briggs. Briggs had been in command of the *Mary Celeste* and was one of the missing men.

Thirty-eight years old, Briggs was a Massachusetts man and a member of a seafaring family. In preparation for this trip, he had come down to New York in early October. Like many another captain setting out on a long voyage, he had decided to take part of his family with him. In mid-October his wife, Sarah, and their two-year-old daughter, Sophia, joined him aboard the *Mary Celeste*. Mrs. Briggs brought along clothes, toys, her melodeon, and her sewing machine. A son, Arthur, was staying with his Grandmother Briggs so that he could go to school.

Captain Briggs signed on seven men for the voyage. The first mate, the second mate, and the steward-cook were Americans. The four seamen were German or Scandinavian. Briggs was well pleased with his crew.

The cargo for this trip was 1,700 barrels of alcohol, which were being shipped to an Italian company in Genoa. While the cargo was being loaded, an accident occurred. A sling slipped and one of the ship's two boats was smashed. There was

o time to replace the boat before the *Mary Celeste*
ailed.

In early November the *Mary Celeste* drew away
rom her pier in the East River. It was the unre-
narkable departure of a small ship on a routine
oyage. There was no hint of what was to come,
o hint that the *Mary Celeste* would soon be the
enter of one of the sea's most famous mysteries.

The court in Gibraltar found the situation baf-
ing. Obviously, an experienced captain does not
bandon ship without a good reason. Yet what could
he reason have been? The *Mary Celeste* was so
ound that Deveau, with a crew of only two, had
ailed her more than 600 miles.

Deveau and the other men of the *Dei Gratia* told
he court all they knew. The *Mary Celeste* was
xamined by experts. British officials went over her.
A diver inspected her hull. A surveyor of shipping
nspected her topsides. The American Consul at
Gibraltar went through the ship. At his request,
Captain R. W. Shufeldt of the United States Navy
hecked the ship. Little turned up that Deveau had
iot observed and reported.

The investigators found a peculiar mark that ran
around the bow of the ship. Here a strip of wood
about six or seven feet long and an inch and a quar-
er wide was missing. The damage was recent.

Still, it in no way affected the seaworthiness of th
ship.

The investigators examined part of the cargo
They found that something had happened to on
barrel of alcohol. Either it had been tampered witl
and opened or else it had been damaged by move
ment during the voyage.

Several dark brownish-red spots were found o
the deck. Similar spots were found on the starboarc
topgallant rail. So was a mark that looked as if i
had been made by a sharp ax.

Perhaps the strangest thing was the distance tha
the *Mary Celeste* seemed to have traveled by her
self. If she was abandoned on the morning o
November 25, then she traveled between 500 anc
750 miles east and north before being found by
the *Dei Gratia* ten days later. That is extremely
good going for an unmanned ship.

In mid-March the salvage court made its decision
It awarded to the master and crew of the *De*
Gratia a sum of money equal to one-fifth the value
of the *Mary Celeste* and her cargo. The *Mary*
Celeste, with a new captain and crew, sailed on to
Genoa.

The mystery, however, was far from solved
There was still no word of the ten people who hac
sailed aboard the *Mary Celeste*. Nor was there any

explanation of why the ship had been abandoned. In fact, no one could tell what was a clue and what wasn't. Was the mark on the bow a clue or had it nothing to do with the mystery? What about the brownish-red spots? And the open cargo hatch? People chose what they thought were clues and built theories around them.

The chief investigator at Gibraltar was an official named Solly J. Flood. Very early during the salvage hearings, he decided that there had been violence aboard the *Mary Celeste*. At first he seemed to suspect the men of the *Dei Gratia*. Perhaps they had murdered the people aboard the *Mary Celeste* and seized the ship for profit.

This theory soon proved ridiculous. The two ships had been hundreds of miles apart in late November. Captain Morehouse was a man of excellent reputation. And in any case, the possible profit was far too small to offset the risk.

Mr. Flood then settled for mutiny and murder. His clues were the cut in the topgallant rail, which suggested an ax; the brownish-red spots, which could be blood; the sword, which might also have dried blood on it; the mark on the bow, which he felt had been made on purpose; and the damaged barrel of alcohol. As he wrote in his report:

"My own theory or guess is that the crew got at

the alcohol and in the fury of drunkenness murdered the Master, whose name was Briggs, his wife
and child and the chief mate; that they then
damaged the bows of the vessel . . . so as to
induce the Master of any vessel which might pick
them up . . . to think her not worth attempting
to save; and that they did, some time between the
25th November and the 5th December, escape on
board some vessel bound for some North or South
American port or the West Indies."

Even at the time, Mr. Flood's theory did not hold
up very well.

If the crew "in the fury of drunkenness" attacked
the captain and mate, there should have been signs
of the attack. There were no such signs. The ship
was orderly. The stains on the sword were analyzed
and turned out to be rust. The spots on the deck
were not blood either.

As for the injury to the bow, some experts agreed
with Mr. Flood that it had been done on purpose.
Others did not agree. Captain Shufeldt, for one,
believed that the natural bending of the planks in
the bow had caused the wood to splinter. Later,
the action of the sea tore off the splintered strip.

Then, too, a missing strip of wood did not make
the *Mary Celeste* look damaged beyond repair. No
one aboard the *Dei Gratia* had even noticed it.

Also, men do not mutiny for fun. Sometimes they are driven to it because their commander is a tyrant. Sometimes they mutiny out of greed. Aboard the *Mary Celeste* there was no motive for mutiny. Briggs was a decent man, not a tyrant. And there was nothing of value aboard the ship that the men could take.

Supposing, though, that the men did mutiny. What became of them? If they escaped in the *Mary Celeste*'s boat, why did they leave all their own possessions behind? Why didn't they sink the *Mary Celeste*? Afloat she was a piece of damaging evidence against them. Once she was sunk, they could pose as shipwrecked sailors.

Yet, for all its weaknesses, the mutiny-murder theory was widely accepted. The seaports of the world were alerted to keep a lookout for the crew of the *Mary Celeste*. But not a man of them ever turned up. Their families never heard from them again. Nor did anyone else.

A much more likely theory was that the *Mary Celeste* had been abandoned in a moment of panic. The chief clue here was the obvious haste with which her people had left. They had no time to gather even the smallest of their possessions. They had time only to snatch up the ship's papers, the navigation instruments, and some cooked food.

What could have caused such panic?

Captain Morehouse always believed that on the morning of November 25, the wind dropped and the *Mary Celeste* was becalmed. A current caught the ship and carried her toward the rocky, rugged coast of Santa Maria. The men fought to work their ship out of the current, but lost hope as the ship was drawn closer and closer to the threatening shore. Then, with no time to spare, they took to the *Mary Celeste*'s one boat. Unfortunately, they did not make the boat fast to the ship by a line. And, when a breeze sprang up, the ship sailed away from them. Row as they might, the men could not catch the *Mary Celeste*.

Later, Morehouse believed, the small boat was driven into the rocky cliffs and all aboard were drowned.

Captain James Briggs, a brother of the missing master, also believed that this was what had happened. Yet the theory does not really explain the apparent haste with which the ship had been abandoned.

The *Mary Celeste* would have been drifting slowly in the current. Danger would have loomed up gradually, giving them plenty of time to prepare for abandoning ship. Then, too, no experienced captain would order his men and family into a small boat without a line to the ship.

Oliver Deveau thought that the water in the hold was the chief clue to the mystery. The *Mary Celeste* had come through some severe winter storms. She had weathered a gale on November 24. And Deveau, sounding the pumps, had found three and a half feet of water in the hold. He believed that a faulty sounding of the pumps made the water seem much deeper. Convinced that the ship was sinking, the men took to the boat and were later lost.

The trouble with Deveau's theory is that Briggs would not have made such a mistake. Nor would he have panicked on a fair, calm morning.

Admitting this, some people have suggested that Briggs was already dead. Perhaps he had been swept overboard. Perhaps he had died of an illness. Without their captain, the men panicked and hastily launched the ship's boat.

This does not seem likely either. Any accident to the captain would have been noted in the logbook, but no such note was there.

The most likely solution to the mystery is the one suggested by Briggs's cousin, Dr. Oliver Cobb, who was a boy of fourteen when the *Mary Celeste* sailed in 1872. Dr. Cobb decided that the chief clues were the cargo—the 1,700 barrels of alcohol—and the open cargo hatch.

Normally, such a cargo, properly stored, should be perfectly safe. But under certain conditions, the cargo could give off gases. In a warm cargo hold, some small explosions might occur. And these might touch off a general explosion. A small ship like the *Mary Celeste* would be blown to pieces by the explosion of 1,700 barrels of alcohol. Here, then, was real cause for panic. Perhaps events went something like this:

The morning of November 25, 1872, was clear and warm, with a light wind blowing. The *Mary Celeste*, slipping quietly through the ocean swells, would soon leave the Azores behind.

In early or midmorning, someone noticed a danger signal. Perhaps he smelled gas near the cargo hatch. Perhaps he heard a rumbling in the cargo hold. The captain ordered the hatch removed to let air into the hold.

The men began to lift the hatch. As they did so, there may have been a great rush of fumes and gas, accompanied by a deep-throated roar. There may even have been a small explosion. Either would have made it seem that the ship might blow up at any moment.

Alarm and confusion reigned. Some men began

to take in sail. Others started to launch the ship's only boat. Then they heard even louder rumbling or a second small explosion. There was not a minute to waste—no time to take in sail, no time to lash the wheel. The captain snatched up his navigating instruments and the ship's papers. Someone else grabbed whatever food was at hand. And all tumbled into the boat.

The boat was small and overcrowded. It may have capsized at once. Or Briggs, with his family and crew, may have got safely off the ship. If they did, their one aim must have been to get as far away from the ship as possible. They rowed with frantic haste, pulling away from that dangerous cargo.

At last it was safe to stop. The men rested their oars and waited. Minutes passed. Nothing happened. They waited and waited. Still nothing happened. Now they were unsure of what to do next—keep away or go back to the ship.

Suddenly the decision was taken out of their hands. The wind freshened. The sails of the *Mary Celeste* filled, and the ship drew away.

Did they row after her, pulling in vain until the sails vanished over the horizon? Or did they head toward shore, only to have their boat wrecked on the rocks? Whatever happened, no trace of them

was ever found. There was only the *Mary Celeste*
sailing on unmanned. The fresh air swept away th
gases, and with them the key to the mystery.

That may well have been what happened. But th
truth vanished with the *Mary Celeste*'s people. Th
ship herself ran aground in January, 1885, o
Roshelle Reef off Haiti. When her timbers rotte
there, nothing was left of the *Mary Celeste* but a
unsolved mystery.

The Curious Case of the
Asiatic Prince

MARCH 16, 1928, was sailing day for the British merchant ship *Asiatic Prince*. By midafternoon she was almost ready to leave. Her tanks were filled with fuel for the diesel engines. The cargo was stowed and the hatches closed. The steel lifeboats and other emergency equipment had been inspected. All was in order. Now, as a tug nosed its way up to the ship, the harbor pilot came aboard.

At four o'clock, precisely on schedule, the mooring lines were cast off. Slowly, the *Asiatic Prince* moved out into Los Angeles harbor, bound for Yokohama, Japan.

It was the most ordinary of departures. The pilot was interested in the ship only because she was new. He found that she handled well but was in no way remarkable. Her master, Captain Duncan, told the

71

pilot that he was very pleased with the *Asiatic Prince*. He had recently sailed her across the Atlantic to Norfolk, Virginia, at a time when the ocean was wild with winter storms. The ship had come through the gales splendidly.

Before long, the *Asiatic Prince* cleared Los Angeles harbor and reached the open waters of the Pacific. The pilot said good-by to the captain and boarded his launch for the trip back to shore. Lights ablaze in the twilight, diesel engines throbbing, the *Asiatic Prince* headed out into the Pacific. If the weather held good, it would not be long before she saw the lights of Yokohama.

The weather, however, did not hold good. Eight days later, a frightful storm was raging several hundred miles off Hawaii. And somewhere in this storm a ship was in trouble.

The British steamer *City of Eastbourne* was wallowing through mountainous waves when her radio operator picked up an SOS call. Two other ships in the area, the *Niagara* and the *Ventura*, picked up the same call. The signal was so faint, though, that none of the ships was able to hear it clearly. They made out the SOS and they thought they understood the words "terrible storm." But they did not hear the position of the ship in trouble.

Without the position, they could not go to her

The *Asiatic Prince* headed out into the Pacific

rescue. So the three ships reported the SOS to the United States Navy in Hawaii. Navy ships then searched the area from which the call had come. They found no trace of a ship or wreckage.

Meanwhile, an odd puzzle was developing.

The ship in trouble had given not her name but the radio call letters assigned to her. The letters, GJVR, were heard by the radio operators of the *City of Eastbourne*, the *Niagara*, and the *Ventura*. They turned out to be the call letters of a tanker, the *British Hussar*.

Authorities then thought they knew what had happened. The long, low tanker had been caught on the crests of two waves—one under her bow, the other under her stern. As she hung there, she had broken in two. This was a fate that had overcome many a tanker in stormy seas. Torn apart, the tanker had sunk so rapidly that her radio operator had been able to send only one short message. There had been no time for him to repeat his call before the ship went down.

The bad news was cabled to the owners of the *British Hussar*.

A surprising answer came back. The *British Hussar*, her owners said, could not possibly have been sinking in the Pacific on March 24. At that time, she was in the Persian Gulf, on the far side of the world. While the Navy was searching for her, the *Hussar* was docking at Abadan. The ship, her owners went on, had not been near the Pacific in recent months. And she had at no time sent out distress signals.

This was an astounding turn of events. There was no doubt about the SOS or the call letters. They had been heard by three different radio operators on three different ships. But what ship had sent the SOS? And why was she using the call letters of the *British Hussar?*

Investigation showed that on March 24 four ships had been in the storm area. Three of them were the *City of Eastbourne*, the *Niagara*, and the *Ventura*. They were all accounted for. Each had survived the storm and arrived at her destination.

The fourth ship was the *Asiatic Prince*. By now she was overdue at Yokohama and had not been heard from.

It was probable, then, that she had sent the SOS.

Further investigation showed that her call signal differed from that of the *British Hussar* by only one letter. The signal of the *Hussar* was GJVR. That of the *Asiatic Prince* was GJVP. In the international wireless code tapped out by ocean-going ships, the difference was simply one of a dash. *P* is dot-dash-dash-dot. *R* is dot-dash-dot.

No one could explain how or why the *Asiatic Prince*'s radio operator had made a mistake in sending his own call letters. But he must have done so. The only other choice was to believe that the call had come from a ship 6,000 miles away with no reason to be sending an SOS.

The big question now was: What had happened to the *Asiatic Prince?*

She was a new ship, a sturdy ship, a ship that had weathered winter storms in the Atlantic. Had she sunk in a gale that three older ships survived without difficulty?

Perhaps she had. Under a heavy pounding, her plates might have buckled. Her propeller shaft might have snapped. Her engines might have stopped. There were many things that could have happened. But none of them would have sunk her immediately. She should have had time to get off more than one brief call for help. That was the strange thing. What could have overwhelmed her? Why was there only one SOS? Why did the radio operator get his own call letters wrong?

There were no answers to those questions. And so rumors and wild theories began to spread through the world of shipping. The *Asiatic Prince* had been swallowed by a giant tidal wave, said one story. She had been overwhelmed by a waterspout, said a second. Struck and destroyed by a meteorite, said a third.

Rumor said that the *Asiatic Prince* had been carrying secret weapons or gold. And this gave rise to the favorite theory: that she had been seized by a gang of Chinese pirates.

At that time, in the 1920's, pirates were extremely active along the coast of China. Twenty or thirty Chinese pirates, carrying hidden arms, would board a ship as passengers. At a moment when no help was near, they attacked. First they seized the radio cabin and silenced the operator. Then they seized the bridge and forced the officers to steer for one of the bays that were pirate bases. There they robbed the passengers, took anything of value that the ship was carrying, and escaped in their own boats.

Many people decided that something of this sort must have happened to the *Asiatic Prince*. Some liked to think that she had been lost not off Hawaii but off the coast of China. There, they said, she was boarded by pirates who murdered the crew, stole the gold, sank the ship, and escaped in their own boats. Others supposed that a gang of Chinese pirates had boarded the *Asiatic Prince* in Los Angeles. Discovered in mid-ocean, the pirates had to attack then, instead of waiting until they were

closer to their homeland. As they rushed the radio
cabin, the operator had time to send out only one
call for help, his haste causing him to get the call
letters wrong. Then the pirates won control of the
ship from the captain and crew.

The pirate theory is exciting but far from likely.
It does not explain what a gang of Chinese pirates
was doing in Los Angeles; how they managed to
board the *Asiatic Prince*, which carried no passengers; or why they were not immediately discovered.
No more does it explain what became of the ship,
the pirates, and the gold—if there was any.

Yet the pirate theory lives on because no official
statement was ever made about the loss of the
Asiatic Prince. No public inquiry was ever held.
And that is the really curious thing about the case
of the *Asiatic Prince*.

Was she carrying gold or secret weapons? Was
she a stable ship? How was her cargo stowed?
Could it have broken loose in a storm, shifted, and
caused her to go over? Was nothing known that
could shed light on her loss?

If there are answers to these questions, they have
never been made public. And this strange silence
makes the loss of a fine new ship and her forty-nine
men an almost clueless mystery.

"Remember the *Maine!*"

FOR SOME years trouble had been brewing in Cuba. Throughout the island, anger smoldered against the harsh, cruel rule of Spanish officials. Occasionally this anger broke into the flames of open rebellion, which Spanish soldiers put down.

The Cuban situation was of concern to the United States. Cuba lay at our doorstep. Millions of American dollars were invested in Cuban industries. American sympathies lay strongly and openly with the Cuban rebels. Spain, naturally, resented this.

On January 15, 1898, Spanish soldiers stirred up riots in Havana. The riots were directed chiefly against the United States.

A few days later the United States battleship *Maine* arrived in Havana Harbor. She was making what the United States Government described as a friendly visit.

79

To Spanish officials in Cuba the *Maine*'s visit
seemed anything but friendly. They saw it as a
threat to themselves and a means of encouraging
the rebels. Still, they behaved courteously, and the
visit proceeded peacefully, with the *Maine* riding
at anchor in Havana Harbor.

The gray, heavy day of February 15 passed
quietly. Night came. The tide changed. And the
Maine swung at anchor with the tide.

Suddenly, at twenty minutes to ten, people near
the harbor heard a sharp report, rather like a gunshot. It was followed by a tremendous explosion.

The *Maine* vanished in a cloud of black smoke. A
column of flames shot skyward through the smoke.

When, several minutes later, the smoke lifted, the
blackened wreck of the ship was seen, still afloat in
the harbor. Her bow was burning furiously. The
stern was crowded with men.

Rescue work began immediately. An American
steamer and a Spanish cruiser lowered boats. They
began to pick up men who had been blown into the
water or who had jumped off the burning ship. Together with the *Maine*'s two undamaged boats, they
took survivors off the stern of the battleship. Even
so, the death roll was high. Out of 354 men, only 100
were saved.

The survivors' stories made clear, in part, what

The report was followed by a tremendous explosion

had happened. There had been an explosion in the forward magazines, an area where a warship's ammunition is stored.

What had touched off the explosion? On that grim night of February 15, 1898, there was no answer to the question. And even today the answer is still cloaked in mystery.

There were only two possibilities.

The cause could have been inside the *Maine* herself. In this case the sinking was an accident.

Or the cause could have been something outside the *Maine*, something like a mine. In this case the sinking was the warlike act of an enemy.

The government in Spain immediately expressed its regret over the "accident" to the *Maine*. Spanish officials in Cuba assured the United States that they knew nothing about the explosion. But almost no one in the United States believed the Spanish officials. Most people were sure that the Spaniards had blown up the *Maine*.

The United States Government announced that it would hold an inquiry on the sinking of the *Maine*.

Spanish officials announced that they, too, would hold an inquiry.

The two inquiries were held and ended with completely different results. The Spanish court

ound that the explosion could not possibly have
been caused by a mine. The American inquiry
ound that it must have been caused by a mine.

The American public had been angry with Spain
o begin with. Now the people were roused to fury,
heir rage fed by the stories published in sensational
ewspapers. There were demands for vengeance.
Men, women, and children wore buttons bearing
he motto, "Remember the *Maine!*" And by late
April the United States was at war with Spain.

Perhaps war would have come in any case. But
here is no doubt that the sinking of the *Maine*
hastened it.

Still, the matter was far from clear-cut. Both
courts had strong arguments to support their find-
ngs.

The American court first took evidence about the
explosion from the survivors.

The captain of the *Maine* told the court that he
had been writing letters in his cabin when he heard
"a bursting, rending and crashing sound or roar of
immense volume." This was followed by a series of
heavy crashes. The lights went out and smoke filled
he ship.

A member of the crew described "a trembling
and buckling of the decks, and then a prolonged
roar." Another crew member had first heard a sharp

report, like a gunshot. He saw a flash of light. Then he said, a second explosion seemed to lift the ship out of the water. An officer had seen "the whole starboard side of the deck spring up into the air" after the explosion.

The accounts differed in detail. But one point was clear. The explosion took place in the forward magazines.

Was there anything in the forward part of the *Maine* which might have set off the explosion?

The court examined the possibilities one by one.

Could a bomb have been smuggled aboard? The answer seemed to be no. The captain had given orders that visitors were to be followed wherever they went aboard ship and carefully watched.

Was anything explosive stored in or near the magazines? Again the answer was no. Items such as torpedo heads were stored aft. Varnish, alcohol, and other such materials were kept well away from the magazines.

Could the boilers have exploded? Once more the answer was no. Since the ship was lying at anchor, only two boilers were working. Both were in good condition. Both were working under low pressure. And both were in another part of the ship.

Could there have been an outbreak of fire in the coal bunkers? This was a serious possibility. Certain materials can and do set fire to themselves through chemical changes. This is called spontaneous combustion. A pile of oily rags may suddenly burst into flames. So may coal, under certain conditions. This had happened in several United States warships.

Had it happened also in the *Maine?* Again the answer seemed to be no. There were six coal bunkers near the forward magazines. Four of them were empty, having just been painted. One was half-full of coal and had been used that very evening. Here the crewmen would have noticed the danger signal of spontaneous combustion—a rise in temperature. The sixth bunker was full. But it had been inspected the day of the explosion. No rise in temperature had been noted.

For all these reasons the American court decided that the explosion had not been set off by anything inside the *Maine.* The cause must have been outside the ship. And the evidence given by a diver led the court to believe that the cause was a mine.

The diver had not got a good look at the bow of the *Maine.* The bow was a tangled mass of steel. And it was settling in the soft mud of the harbor bottom. However, the court accepted two of his findings: that the outer shell of the ship had been forced up about thirty-four feet; and that the out-

side bottom plating had been bent into an upsid
down V. The court believed that this damage cou
have been caused in only one way. A mine mu
have gone off directly under the ship.

However, the Spanish court had found that
mine could not have caused the explosion. As th
court pointed out, only one kind of mine could blo
up a ship at anchor. This was a mine linked to th
shore by a cable. Electric current sent through th
cable would fire the mine. But Spanish divers ha
found no trace of a cable in the harbor. So a mir
could not be blamed.

The court also made these points:

There was no case on record of a mine's havin
exploded a ship's magazine. Mines had sunk ship
yes. But they had never exploded a magazine.

The explosion of a mine always killed a larg
number of fish. The fish were later seen floating o
the surface of the water. Yet not one dead fish ha
been seen in Havana Harbor the morning after th
disaster.

For these reasons, the Spanish court said, th
Maine could not have been sunk by a mine. Th
cause must have been within the ship herself.

There the matter rested. Neither inquiry wa
really satisfactory, for each was limited. Th
Spanish court did not examine either the wreckag

of the *Maine* or the survivors. The American court knew nothing about the harbor bottom or Spanish military equipment. But war came, and for some years no one again investigated the *Maine*.

Then, in 1909, the *Maine* was declared a danger to harbor shipping. United States Army Engineers managed to raise the stern of the battleship. They towed it away to deep water and sank it. Getting at the tangled wreckage of the bow was more difficult. They finally built a cofferdam around it and pumped out the water. The wreckage was then exposed within the watertight dam.

A naval expert examined it. His chief find was a curved bottom plate. Its shape, he said, showed that it had been bent by an outside explosion. One of the *Maine*'s forward magazines had been directly above this plate. The United States Navy Department accepted this finding.

Perhaps, then, the *Maine* was the first ship in history to have its magazines exploded by a mine. But even so, there are many things that no one has ever explained.

There is the question of the noise heard before the explosion. Witnesses described it as a sharp report. That is not the kind of noise a mine makes. A mine explodes with a dull, heavy sound.

If a mine went off under the hull, the ship should

have been heaved up. Upheaval was felt only after the magazines exploded.

Finally, there is the business of the dead fish that should have littered the harbor—and didn't.

Still, the evidence found in the wreckage points to a mine. And so it is possible that something like this happened:

The Spaniards, fearing war, took steps to defend themselves against attack. They armed forts along the coast. And they laid mines in the harbor. Naturally, they would not have used the kind of mines that float and explode on contact. These would have been dangerous to their own ships. Instead, they would have used mines laid in particular places and set off from shore.

With the harbor already mined, Spanish officials learned that the battleship *Maine* was coming to pay an unwelcome visit. What if war should suddenly be declared while an enemy battleship was sitting in their harbor? They decided to protect themselves against this possibility. They assigned the *Maine* an anchorage that was mined.

Since the weeks of the visit passed quietly, it is unbelievable that Spanish officials decided to explode the mine. The act would have gained them nothing, and would have been an invitation to war.

It is much more likely that temptation became

too great for someone in the Spanish defense forces. On the night of February 15, he looked out into the harbor. The *Maine* had swung with the tide. Her guns now pointed at the Spanish defenses. He saw by the electrical gear ashore that the *Maine* had come in contact with a mine. His hand moved—and the deed was done.

Spanish officials must have quickly learned what had happened. The question then is: Why didn't they confess, apologize, and offer to pay damages? This was their only chance to prevent war. By denying their guilt, they made war certain.

The case of the *Maine* has long been closed. But the questions without answers live on in the minds of all who remember the *Maine*.

The Riddle of the *Flying Enterprise*

As THE year 1951 drew to a close, a series of terrible storms swept the North Atlantic and battered western Europe. Seas lashed the coasts and flooded low-lying areas. Airports closed down. And out on the sea itself winter winds howled and blew without cease. Under leaden skies the gray-green water was surly, sullen, and angry. Waves surged across it, their crests whipped white by hurricane-force winds.

Such a sea is hungry for ships. A German freighter went down off Borkum in the North Sea. A Dutch tanker sank in the Bay of Biscay. So did a Norwegian tanker. The master and third mate of another Norwegian ship were lost when a huge wave ripped off her bridge. A small British steamer was blown out of the water onto the coast of western Scotland. The giant passenger liner *Queen Mary*

ought her way safely across the Atlantic but arrived
hree days late.

Still, ships continued to sail out of the sheltered
afety of harbors, to challenge the sea in its most
avage of moods. Among them was the American
reighter *Flying Enterprise*.

In the German ports of Bremen and Hamburg
he had taken on a mixed cargo of pig-iron bars,
Volkswagens, machines, pianos, antiques, and other
general cargo. She was also carrying hundreds of
mailbags. On December 21, 1951, the *Flying Enterprise* left Hamburg, bound for New York. Aboard
were ten passengers and a crew of forty. Her captain was a Danish-born American named Kurt Carlsen.

Raging winds and vicious seas rolled the *Flying
Enterprise* about for the first four days of the voyage. Christmas found her some 300 miles southwest
of Ireland, battling one of the worst gales in twenty-
five years. December 26 brought even worse
weather. Now it was no longer a question of forging
ahead through the storm. It was a question of holding one's own, of riding it out until the storm began
to weaken.

But it was the ship that weakened first.

Above the snarl of the wind, above the groaning
and creaking of the ship, a dull rumble was heard

below decks. The ship heeled over to port and did not fully right herself.

In the cargo hold the iron bars had broken loose and shifted to the port side.

Hours later a gigantic wave smashed against the *Flying Enterprise*, pounding and straining her. Three cracks opened in her deck. Water poured into the number 3 cargo hold. Throbbing pumps at first controlled the flooding, but then the water began to rise in the hold.

The iron bars continued to rumble deep within the ship. Nothing could be done about them. Men attempting to secure them would have been crushed to death. The list grew worse, as the cargo shifted more to port.

From the wheelhouse came the worst of news: Rudder stuck fast!

The *Flying Enterprise* had ceased to be a sturdy ship fighting the storm. She was a cripple, lying helpless in the hungry sea.

Carlsen ordered the radio operator to send an SOS. The message crackled out: SOS, SOS. *Flying Enterprise* drifting rudderless. Have 30-degree list. Situation grave.

Miles away, that December 28, other storm-tossed ships heard the call for help. In the battle against the sea, all men are brothers. The ships

.tered course and slowly beat their way toward
ıe stricken freighter.

Aboard the *Flying Enterprise* everything was on
slant. Nowhere was there a level surface. The
oilers had long since gone out. The interior of the
ıip was as bitterly cold as the outdoors, though it
ffered shelter from the wind and rain. Passengers,
orced to leave flooded cabins, huddled wherever
ıey could. The crew, red-eyed and weary from
ıck of sleep, waged a desperate battle against a
elentless enemy.

Carlsen had no idea how much longer his ship
vould stay afloat. And so, as the rescue ships began
ɔ arrive, he faced a difficult decision. He had to get
is passengers and crew off before the *Flying Enter-
rise* sank. At the same time, he could not ask the
ther ships to lower boats in a sea that was certain
ɔ overwhelm them. Somehow he must choose just
he right moment.

By Saturday, December 29, five ships were stand-
ng by. And, finally, the wind had dropped. The
ea was still stormy. The wind still blew, but it was
ιo longer at gale force. Now was the time.

The American steamer *Southland* called the *Fly-
ng Enterprise* on her short-wave set. "Shall we send
•ver a boat?"

Carlsen answered, "Please send a boat and pour

oil on the water. I am sending off passengers an(
crew."

Volunteers prepared to lower the *Southland*
motor launch. Aboard the United States troop trans
port *General A. W. Greely,* volunteers readied a
second boat for launching. The other ships tha
were standing by lined up to form a kind of break
water. They pumped oil to calm the sea. Soon th(
water gleamed black. The long, white fingers o
searchlights played on its surface.

The deck of the *Flying Enterprise* was lined wit!
figures in life jackets. Carlsen mustered the crew
and chose the best swimmers. Each was assigned t(
jump into the water with a passenger and make
sure the passenger reached one of the boats.

Two by two, figures jumped into the oily winte1
sea. The rest of the crew followed. Within minute;
they were safe aboard the *Southland* and the *Gree*
ly. Only Carlsen remained on the *Flying Enter-*
prise. He talked by radio with the *Southland* an(
the *Greely,* making sure that everyone was accounted for.

As Carlsen went back on deck to jump, he notice(
that his ship was steadying. With a sudden surge o'
hope, he decided to stay aboard and do what h(
could to save her. While she floated, the *Flying En-*

erprise was his ship, his responsibility. She was his
o nurse, his to command. He would leave her when
all hope was gone and not before. He notified the
other ships of his decision.

Four of the five rescue ships sailed off. The
arrangement was that one would stay behind until
the United States destroyer *J. W. Weeks* arrived to
relieve her. The destroyer was to stay with the *Flying Enterprise* until she either sank or was taken in
tow.

Aboard the crippled freighter Carlsen steeled
himself to wait. He found some raisin cakes that
the cook had baked for New Year's and took them
to his cabin. They were his chief food for the next
few days. That night, without light or heat, Carlsen wedged himself in a corner of his slanting cabin.
He had long been an amateur wireless enthusiast.
Now, using emergency batteries, he opened up his
set and spoke to the ship standing by.

"For me things have been reduced to a single
problem," he said. "I can only crawl about because
of the ship's list, but I intend to remain aboard as
long as I can. I am responsible for the ship and the
cargo. But now I'm going to try and get some
sleep. I'm dog-tired. I haven't closed my eyes for
four nights. I'm sorry to have caused you embarrass-

ment by remaining on board so that you have t
stand by. I shall make as few demands on you a
possible."

Then he shut down the set and went to sleep.

Sunday and Monday crept past. By Tuesda
morning, New Year's Day, the J. W. Weeks ha
arrived. Commander Thompson maneuvered th
destroyer close to the listing, heaving freighter
Then the Weeks shot a rocket line to the Flying En
terprise and used it to send Carlsen thermos flask
of hot coffee, sandwiches, and candy.

During the day the wind began to rise again
Waves rolled under the freighter, flinging he
about. Carlsen crawled slowly and painfully aroun
the ship. He was bruised by collisions with meta
fittings. He was hungry and tired and sodden wit
sea water and rain. He was worn out from th
struggle to keep his balance on a ship listing at
45-degree angle. He could not wash or bathe o
shave. Nowhere was there warmth. The ship offere
nothing except shelter from the bite of the wind
He braced himself in corners and dozed. He read
book called The Seaman and the Law. And he mus
have thought of his wife and two young daughter
waiting and waiting in Woodbridge, New Jersey.

Around him the sea hugged the ship with eage
arms while the wind howled and beat against her

Under the wind's attack, the *Flying Enterprise* was drifting south and east. This was the only good thing about the situation. She was drifting toward land.

Meanwhile, her owners had finally managed to find a tug. In this weather most of the big, powerful tugs were already hard at work towing in crippled ships. However, the British tug *Turmoil* had just finished one job and was now free to go after the *Flying Enterprise*.

At 11 P.M. on the night of January 3, the *Turmoil* arrived, but nothing could be done before morning. Through the night, Captain Dan Parker of the *Turmoil* pondered the problem that faced him—how to get a heavy towline aboard the *Flying Enterprise*.

Normally, a rescue tug fires a light line across, using a line-firing gun or a rocket. The light line is the first of a series of lines, each heavier than the one before. Several men, heaving and hauling together, pull in the lines until the thick towline comes aboard. It is made fast and then the towing can begin. But this is a job for several men—and Carlsen was alone. He was alone on a slanting, slippery deck that offered no foothold.

Morning brought no solution. The weather was far too bad to risk sending men over to the *Flying Enterprise*. A small boat would be crushed against

the freighter before the men could scramble o
board. Yet there was no time to waste. Wors
weather was forecast for the near future.

Carlsen signaled that he would try to do the jo
alone.

The *Turmoil* edged in. A sharp report echoe
through the air and a line shot onto the deck of th
freighter. Carlsen made a breakneck dash over th
treacherous deck and grabbed the line. He brace
himself as best he could on the slanting, heavin
deck and began to haul.

The first part of the line came in quickly, for i
was light. But soon the weight of the towing line
the hawser, began to tell. Its thick body was mad
of strands of steel wire. Gasping for breath, hi
arms tearing at his shoulder muscles, Carlsen haule
the huge line out of the ocean. Inch by inch, th
great spliced eye in the hawser came closer to him
From the tug men watched with stunned admira
tion. None would have believed that one man coul
handle the towline.

Now, body bowed with strain, Carlsen had hi
hands on the eye. Breath rasping in his throat, h
hauled it over the deck railing. Suddenly hi
strength failed. He could do no more. The hawse
splashed back into the sea.

It was the first of several tries. Once Carlsen came

within two feet of securing the eye aboard the *Flying Enterprise*. This time, too, the strain of hauling the heavy line proved too much for one man who was bracing himself on a wet, slanting, tossing deck. The line fell back.

No one on the *Turmoil* wanted to give up. But it was clear that Carlsen, singlehanded, would never get the hawser on board.

Young Kenneth Dancy, the *Turmoil's* first mate, made a daring and courageous suggestion. If Captain Parker would take the *Turmoil* alongside the *Flying Enterprise*, Dancy would jump aboard the freighter.

Parker did not wish to risk Dancy's life. Yet there seemed no other way to put a tow on the *Flying Enterprise*. The sea was still far too rough for launching a boat.

Parker took the *Turmoil* in on a trial run. The maneuver demanded perfect judgment, perfect timing, and nerves of iron. For only one ship was under control. The listing freighter lurched, swooped, and swung around at the whim of the sea. Parker, to avoid collision, had to judge where the sea would next toss the freighter and how it would affect his tug.

The trial run over, Parker again brought the *Turmoil* in. A distance of ten yards lay between the

two ships. Dancy climbed to the tug's rail an
stood there, balanced by two shipmates. The *Tur
moil* rose on the crest of a wave and clanged agains
the freighter. Dancy stepped out, caught the iror
rail of the freighter, and swung himself aboard
Carlsen grasped his hand.

By then darkness was falling and little more coul
be done that day. Dancy settled down to shar
Carlsen's cold, wet life aboard the *Flying Enter
prise*.

At the first gleam of wintry dawn, the *Turmoil*
rocket gun fired. The line shot onto the *Flying En
terprise*. And this time the hawser was made fast.

The *Turmoil's* propellers bit into the stormy sea
Tug and freighter, escorted by the destroyer, begar
to move slowly toward port. They were some 30C
miles from Falmouth, England, and creeping forward at a speed of three knots.

The *Turmoil* was capable of much greater speed
But Parker did not dare put too much strain on the
freighter. If the cracks in her deck lengthened, he
might tear her in two. However, though the weather
was sullen, the sea was calmer. The slow voyage
proceeded so steadily that by January 8 they had
covered two thirds of the distance to Falmouth.
Victory over the sea was almost within reach.

But the sea was not yet ready to give up its vic-

m. That afternoon another storm started to blow
p. For nine hours the weather got steadily worse.
oncern grew aboard the *Turmoil* and aboard the
estroyer *Willard Keith*, which had relieved the
Veeks. Solid seas were sweeping over the *Flying
Enterprise*. Wind and sea slammed broadside into
he freighter, causing her to drift in spite of the *Tur-
oil*.

At 1:30 in the morning of January 9, the towline
napped.

The sea had snatched back the *Flying Enterprise*,
nd in this weather it was impossible to pass another
ow. The *Turmoil* could do nothing except stand by.

The long hours of darkness wore on. The *Flying
Enterprise* pitched and rolled. The two men aboard
er could feel that she was becoming sluggish. It
ook her longer and longer to recover from a roll.

Dawn came, and the men of the *Turmoil* and
Keith could see that there was no hope of passing
he freighter a new tow. Her bow was well down
n the water. The list was worse. Her port rail was
o badly awash that Carlsen and Dancy could no
onger get near it. Heavy seas washed over her and
ach left her a little lower in the water. Only her
drift was good. She was drifting toward Falmouth.

January 9 passed. The first daylight of January 10
howed that the end was near. The wind was at gale

force. Towering seas crashed down on the *Flying Enterprise*. She was lying low in the water and her list was much more severe.

By midafternoon Carlsen and Dancy knew that the end had come. They were only forty-three miles from land, but the freighter was so far over that she was shipping water down her funnel. At any moment now she would go.

The two men crawled out along the funnel. The plan had been to have them picked off the ship by helicopter. But as they clung to their slippery perch the destroyer flashed them a message. The weather was too bad for the helicopter to rescue them.

The *Turmoil* immediately moved in.

Carlsen and Dancy stood up on the funnel. Dancy knew that Carlsen, as captain, would want to be the last man to leave the ship. Dancy stepped into the water. Carlsen followed.

Nine minutes later they were clambering out of the icy, angry sea up a ladder onto the *Turmoil's* deck.

At 4:11 that afternoon the bow of the *Flying Enterprise* rose fifteen feet out of the raging sea. Then the freighter slipped under and vanished. For Carlsen, standing on the deck of the *Turmoil*, it was the worst moment of the whole ordeal.

In New York, Hans Isbrandtsen, owner of the

Flying Enterprise, wept as a bell tolled in his office to mark the death of a fine ship. In Woodbridge, Mrs. Carlsen wept with joy that her husband was safe.

Carlsen and Dancy arrived at Falmouth to find themselves heroes. During the past thirteen days, the whole world had followed the story of the *Flying Enterprise*, had followed the gallant fight to save her.

Now commercial offers were poured upon the two men. Carlsen was offered $100,000 for his story. Agents of dozens of companies crowded into Falmouth, offering any sum if Carlsen would appear in their advertisements. Similar offers were made to Dancy.

Carlsen and Dancy would have none of it. Carlsen said, "I do not want to have the efforts of two honest men to save a ship commercialized in any way." He said, "I don't want my attempt cheapened. It is a matter of principle." They made clear that they had done their duty, no more, no less. They could not accept rewards for that. All they wanted was peace, and a chance to go back to sea.

In time they got what they wanted. The searchlight of publicity turned away from them. Other stories filled the newspapers. The story of the *Flying Enterprise* seemed to have ended.

Yet one more chapter remained to be written. And this suddenly added a note of mystery to a story of courage and devotion to duty.

In the summer of 1953 the Italian salvage ship *Rostro* appeared in the English Channel, forty-three miles southeast of Falmouth. She had been hired to salvage the cargo of the *Flying Enterprise*.

This came as a great surprise to the shipping world. Salvaging sunken cargo is expensive. No one attempts it unless the cargo is of great value. What valuable cargo ·had the *Flying Enterprise* been carrying? So far as was known, she had been carrying only a mixed, general cargo that would not be worth bringing up from the bottom of the ocean.

Smelling a story, newspapermen tried to find out what was going on. They failed almost completely. The salvage operation was carried out in secret. The *Rostro*'s crew of twenty-seven men had been sworn to secrecy. And no one would say what the cargo was or who wanted it saved.

Kurt Carlsen was questioned, but he had no idea what the salvage ship was seeking. If cargo is valuable, that is the shipper's business, not the captain's. Nor did the Isbrandtsen Company know anything.

On August 28 reporters picked up their first bit of information. After several weeks of work, the *Rostro* had delivered its first load of salvage to the Belgian

The salvage operation was carried out in secret

port of Ostend. Among other things it delivered some $200,000 worth of British and American bank notes. The sodden money was sent to a bank in Brussels to be dried out.

With this discovery the mystery only deepened.

The director of the bank refused to talk about how much money had been shipped on the *Flying Enterprise.* He refused to say whether or not the ship was carrying gold.

A salvage expert pointed out that even such a large sum of money would not make the salvage job worth while. The *Flying Enterprise* was lying in 250 feet of water. It is difficult for divers to work at that depth. They must use special suits or diving bells. So the secret job that the *Rostro* was doing must have been both difficult and very costly.

"There must be something more than bank notes in the ship," the salvage expert told reporters. "It would hardly be worth while sending a specially equipped salvage team out for several weeks only to recover that amount of money."

Rumor said that a diver had brought up six metal boxes which had immediately been flown to Washington, D.C. A Russian journal, *Red Fleet,* published a story saying that the *Flying Enterprise* had been carrying top-secret military instruments. A similar story came from a Swiss source.

The rumors may or may not have been true. It is certain only that the *Flying Enterprise* was carrying something that was of great value to an unnamed group of men, and that this mysterious cargo had nothing to do with Carlsen's gallant fight to save his ship.

The Last of the Five-Masters

IN THE days of sail, many big ships went missing. They sailed a lonely path, seeking out great winds to blow them on their way. From time to time, ships fell victim to these winds. Gales blew them onto shoals. Storms destroyed them. And when the wind failed, currents drew them onto rocks. Yet the fault was more in the times than in the ships, many of which were splendidly built. When weather went against them, they were helpless, for they had no engines. When weather overwhelmed them, they vanished mysteriously, for they had no radios.

So it is strange that the last of the great five-masted, square-rigged ships also vanished without a trace. For this happened in modern times, and the ship carried radio, engine, and all the lifesaving equipment she could possibly need.

The ship was the *København*, a Danish vessel

named for her home port of Copenhagen. And, at the time of her loss in 1928 or 1929, the *København* was the largest and finest sailing ship in the world.

She was built as a school ship for the Danish East Asiatic Company, which believed in sail-training for its future officers. And she was everything that a ship could be. A big, graceful, five-masted ship of steel, she was 430 feet long and strongly built. Her holds were divided by steel partitions into watertight compartments. She had five miles of standing rigging, all of it strong, steel wire. Her twenty-three miles of running rigging was also mostly wire. She carried a powerful diesel engine, to give the cadets engine-room experience. Her long-range radio equipment could send for 1,200 miles. She carried more than enough boats and lifesaving gear for those aboard.

Launched in 1921, the *København* made nine long and successful voyages. She handled magnificently in every kind of weather. Yet she vanished without a trace in December, 1928, or January, 1929.

On what was to be her tenth and last voyage, the *København* sailed from Denmark, bound first for Buenos Aires, Argentina. At the time, there was no cargo for her to carry back to Denmark from Argentina. So she was ordered to proceed to southern Australia, where she would load grain for England.

On December 14, 1928, the *København* sailed from
Buenos Aires.

Her crew numbered sixty. Of these, forty-five
were cadets, boys in their late teens, all of whom
knew the ship well. The remaining men were all
professional seamen.

The captain, Hans Ferdinand Andersen, planned
to follow a route that the *København* had taken
before. It lay to the far south, where the big square-
rigger would be driven forward by westerly storm
after westerly storm. The westerlies were likely to
howl and rage for days on end, but their ways had
been familiar to captains for hundreds of years.
They were not to be feared but sought after for the
speed they would give a sailing ship.

The southern route also held the danger of ice-
bergs. From time to time, huge, flat-topped bergs,
perhaps several miles long, floated up from the Antarctic. But most could easily be seen from afar.

The southern route, then, held its risks, but they
were risks readily accepted. There was really no
other route for a big sailing ship to take. Farther
north, away from the westerlies and the iceberg
zone, there was not enough wind for a big ship.
Besides, many other sailing ships ran the same
course, and the *København* was a finer, safer ship
than any of them.

So she sailed on December 14, early summer south of the equator. All hands were looking forward to Christmas at sea and a quick, pleasant voyage to Australia.

About a week later the *København* was in touch by radio with the Norwegian steamer *William Blumer*. Both ships were then about 1,000 miles from Buenos Aires. The *København* reported that all was well aboard. After that she was not heard from again.

At first the *København*'s radio silence caused no anxiety. She was not under orders to report every day. When the silence continued, there was still no concern. It seemed much more likely that she had had a radio breakdown than that anything had happened to the ship.

But then, after six or seven weeks, the *København* became due in Australia, and there was still no word from her. Mid-February came and went. The big five-master was overdue. There was no sign of her and no news from her. All attempts to reach her by radio failed.

It seemed likely that she had been delayed, perhaps by a storm. Even so, the silence was strange and somewhat worrisome. The owners began getting in touch with all ships that had recently sailed the same route. Reports from these ships said there had been no bad storms. There had been some big ice, but that was normal for the time of year. None, however, could give any news of the *København*.

By late March the *København* was seriously overdue. Clearly, something had happened to her. Perhaps she had lost her masts in a gale. Perhaps she had lost her rudder and had her radio smashed. So the owners set in motion a vast search in the lonely reaches of the far south of the earth. Here were no regular shipping routes where a crippled, drifting ship would soon be sighted. Here were only great open stretches of water, dotted by barren, gale-swept islands. Some of these islands were far south of the *København*'s route. But since she might have drifted toward them, they, too, had to be searched.

The East Asiatic Company sent a big cargo liner to make a thorough search of these islands. She was to search even the most distant—islands like Prince Edward and the Crozets. The search ended in failure. There was no sign of a crippled ship, no sign of wreckage, and no sign of survivors. Food stored on those islands for castaways had not been touched.

Other ships took up the search. Whalers, sealers, tramps, and freighters passing through the area were asked to look for the *København*. The owners kept seeking another ship that might have heard from her earlier. A British steamer, the *City of*

Auckland, reported having heard the *København* using her radio at ten o'clock on the night of December 21. But that was all. Apparently no ship had heard her after that. No ship had heard an SOS. No ship had sighted wreckage or even an empty boat. Nor did the searchers find any trace of her.

The East Asiatic Company refused to give up. Antarctic waters are wide and lonely. There was still a chance that the *København* was somewhere there. She could still be afloat. She was a stout ship, a sturdy ship, a better ship by far than the others that had sailed her route.

Two steamers searched still more tiny islands. Then the company chartered the *Mexico* to search again every island in the region. Along with two other ships, the *Mexico* went wherever a ship could go. The three steamed close to shores of jagged rock and towering cliffs, blasting their sirens and firing signal guns. No trace was found of the *København* or her men.

As is always true when a ship goes missing, a number of false clues turned up. Each was carefully checked and found worthless. Only one seemed to offer any hope and it was carefully investigated.

A missionary on the remote island of Tristan da Cunha said that he had seen a ship in distress on January 21, 1929. The ship had five masts. Her hull

was painted black with a broad white band circling
it. He had not seen any sign of life aboard. The ship,
the missionary said, was drifting, her sails curiously
shortened. When last seen, she was heading for the
reefs off Tristan.

If the missionary was right, the ship must have
been the *København*. Her hull colors were black
and white. More important, she was then the only
five-masted vessel afloat.

Investigation cast doubt on whether the missionary had correctly counted the masts. It showed that
a four-masted Finnish ship, the *Ponape*, did pass
Tristan da Cunha on the afternoon of January 21.
But she carried a full crew, had suffered no damage,
and was not in distress. She had been sailing safely
past the island, about six miles out.

Others on the island reported seeing the four-
master, but they had not seen a five-masted ship.

No one, however, wanted to pass up the slightest
chance of finding the *København*. So a British
steamer visited the reefs and part of the island where
the ship had been reported. Again there was no trace
of her, no sign that any ship had ever been wrecked
there.

The East Asiatic Company kept on searching.
For more than a year, ships followed, crossed, and
recrossed the *København*'s probable route. They

Her hull colors were black and white

checked islands, beaches, reefs, rocks—every place
where the wreckage of a ship might have caught.
Never before in history had there been such a search
of the far south. But it was all in vain.

In Denmark an inquiry was held. It could add
nothing to what was known. Men who had earlier
sailed in the *København* told the court that she was
an excellent ship with no weaknesses. They could
not even guess what might have happened to her.
Nor could anyone else. The court could find only
that she had gone down so quickly that no SOS
could be sent and no boats lowered. Why she went
down the court could not say. The reason is anyone's
guess.

Perhaps she was caught in a violent and sudden
shift of wind. Then, with her sails taken aback and
thundering against the steel masts, she heeled far
over, could not recover, and went down within
seconds. Such swift, sudden accidents have given
other ships to the sea.

Or perhaps an iceberg sent her to her doom.
A berg shows little of its bulk. Most of it lies hidden
beneath the ocean's surface. Its hidden, jagged horns
of ice are hard enough to rip the toughest steel like
paper. The *København*, driven through the night by
a gale, may have gone down in an instant, her bottom slashed by ice.

In either case, there would have been no time. No time for an SOS. No time for boats. And there would have been nothing left. With the ship running before a gale wind, everything on deck would have been lashed down. She would sink without a clue. Nothing would wash away. Nothing would be cast up to tell the searchers what had happened.

But all this is guesswork. The loss of the *København* with all her fine young men remains one of the great and clueless mysteries of the sea.

"It is all my fault"

ON THE warm Thursday evening of June 22, 1893, Lady Tryon was entertaining some 200 guests at her home in London. Several of the guests, it was later said, distinctly saw the familiar figure of Vice-Admiral Sir George Tryon moving about at the party. Chatting with Lady Tryon, they mentioned their surprise and pleasure at seeing Sir George. But Lady Tryon assured them that they were mistaken. Her husband was still on duty as Commander-in-Chief of the British Mediterranean Squadron. Lady Tryon herself had only returned from visiting him three weeks before.

The dreadful news, of course, had not yet reached London and would not arrive until early the next morning. But, at the time of Lady Tryon's party, Sir George was dead. That afternoon his flagship, the battleship *Victoria*, had collided with another battleship, the *Camperdown*. The *Victoria* had sunk, taking with her the admiral, twenty-two officers, and more than 300 men.

There was no mystery about what had happened. The *Camperdown*, obeying an order from Tryon's flagship, rammed and sank the *Victoria*. But how and why that fatal order came to be given was then—and remains to this day—very much of a mystery.

The main facts were brought out at the court-martial set up to inquire into the collision.

At quarter to ten on the morning of June 22, the British Mediterranean Squadron weighed anchor at Beirut and steamed out to sea. Its next port of call was Tripoli, about sixty miles up the coast of Syria.

The trip was short; the fleet would be anchoring again by four-thirty in the afternoon. The summer day hung heavy over the Mediterranean. But with Tryon in command no one could afford to relax. The admiral was famous for ordering unexpected and unfamiliar maneuvers. This was his way of keeping peacetime officers alert and in fighting trim. This was his way of preparing men for battle conditions and enemy surprises.

Few of his officers ever understood what Tryon had in mind, and he never explained his plans beforehand. It was his custom to explain the maneuvers after they had been carried out. When signal flags were hoisted on the *Victoria,* the captains of other ships were expected both to obey and to think for themselves.

Early in afternoon of June 22, Admiral Tryon sent for the *Victoria's* captain, Maurice Bourke, and the staff commander, Thomas Hawkins-Smith. He announced that the fleet was to maneuver before anchoring.

Up till then, the thirteen ships had been steaming north spread out in a line two miles wide. Tryon ordered the formation changed. The fleet was to re-form into two columns, line ahead.

The *Camperdown,* commanded by Rear Admiral Albert Hastings Markham, was to lead the port (left) column. The *Victoria* would lead the starboard (right) column. The two columns were to maintain

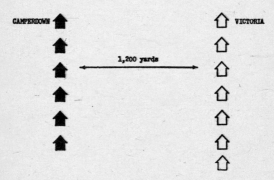

The formation that Tryon ordered

a distance of six cables, or 1,200 yards, between hem.

The two columns were to steam past the place Tryon had chosen for anchoring. Then, led by the *Camperdown* and the *Victoria*, each column was to turn inward. While keeping the order of the fleet, the ships were to reverse their course. They would then steam back to the chosen place and drop anchor.

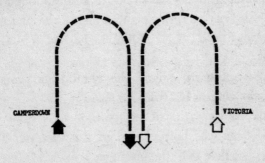

The maneuver as Hawkins-Smith and others understood it

As Tryon announced this maneuver, Hawkins-Smith began to worry about the distance between the two columns. He believed the distance was dangerously short. If the *Victoria* and *Camperdown* turned inward, they would be almost sure to collide.

Staff commanders do not argue with admirals, though, especially with admirals as brilliant as Tryon. However, before leaving, Hawkins-Smith did

suggest that perhaps the distance should be in-
creased to eight cables.

Without appearing to give the matter much
thought, Tryon replied, "Yes, it shall be eight cables."

But later, giving instructions to Lord Gillford,
the flag lieutenant, Tryon returned to his original
plan. He plainly stated that the distance was to be
six cables. In fact, he scribbled the figure 6 on a
piece of paper and handed it to Gillford.

Hesitantly, the officers once more questioned the
admiral. Was his order eight cables, as he had told
Hawkins-Smith, or six cables as he had told Gillford?

"Leave it at six cables," the admiral said, annoy-
ance showing in his voice.

Gillford gave the necessary orders. A series of
signal flags was hoisted aboard the *Victoria*. The
rest of the fleet read the message:

"Second division alter course in succession 16
points to starboard, preserving the order of the
fleet; and the first division alter course in succession
16 points to port, preserving the order of the fleet."

On eleven of the ships, the order, though puz-
zling, presented no great problem. These ships had
only to follow the *Victoria* or *Camperdown* and do
what they did.

Aboard the *Camperdown*, the order presented an

enormous problem. Admiral Markham and Captain Johnstone did not know what to make of it. "It is impossible!" the admiral exclaimed. Johnstone agreed. If the two battleships turned inward toward each other, they would be on a collision course.

Markham stood debating the order with himself. Finally he decided to signal that he had not understood it.

Meanwhile, aboard the *Victoria*, Tryon waited impatiently for the *Camperdown* to acknowledge the signal. The ships were fast approaching shore. There was no time to waste. He signaled the *Camperdown*: "What are you waiting for?"

Markham and Johnstone decided that the maneuver must be attempted. There was no longer time to question the order. Probably Admiral Tryon had a plan which they did not understand, a plan which would avoid collision. The thing to do was to obey the order.

The *Camperdown* signaled that the order was understood.

The two battleships began to turn inward.

Tryon was staring out over the stern of the *Victoria*. His eyes were fixed on the fleet, watching to see how the ships were maneuvering. "An admiral's eyes should be aft and the captain's forward," he had often told Bourke.

Bourke's eyes were forward, noting how the *Camperdown* and the *Victoria* were closing on each other. Trying to hide his anxiety, Bourke said to the admiral, "We shall be very close to that ship, sir."

Tryon seemed not to hear him. The *Victoria* steamed on, coming closer and closer to the *Camperdown.*

Bourke spoke again. "We had better do something, sir. We shall be too close to the *Camperdown.*"

Again the admiral made no reply.

Was the admiral ignoring him? Or was Tryon concentrating so hard on the fleet that he was deaf to all else? Bourke could not tell. "We must do something, sir!" he said. "May I go astern with the port screw?"

Twice more Bourke asked permission to reverse one engine—to slow the *Victoria* and swing her away from the *Camperdown.*

At last Admiral Tryon answered him and gave permission.

Immediately the port engine was reversed. Soon after, Bourke ordered the starboard engine also reversed.

On the *Camperdown* the same orders had been given.

It was too late. Slowly, steadily the two great ships advanced on each other.

At precisely 3:34 P.M. the *Camperdown* crashed into the bow of the *Victoria*, grinding and ripping her way through the flagship's armor.

On the other ships of the fleet, men watching in helpless horror saw the *Victoria* heave sideways, heard the terrible scream of metal against metal, and saw the *Camperdown* slowly back away.

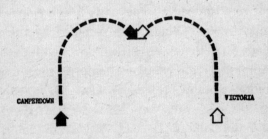

The maneuver as it took place

Aboard the *Victoria* perfect discipline was maintained. Sick men were brought up on deck. Prisoners were released from the guardroom. The crew carried out their orders, attempting to save the stricken ship.

The *Victoria* was badly hurt, but those aboard had no reason to think that she would sink immediately. Tryon decided to make for the shore and beach his ship.

Within ten minutes he knew the *Victoria* would

never make shore. He signaled for the other ships to send boats.

To the very end discipline held aboard the battle ship. Her men stood their ranks on deck. Not one moved until an officer shouted the order, "Jump!" The *Victoria* was by then going down, capsizing to starboard.

The engines were still working as she sank. Many men were trapped at their posts in the engine and furnace rooms. Others were mangled by the propellers. Still others were sucked down with the ship.

Admiral Tryon made no attempt to save himself. Standing on the bridge, he went down with his ship. His last words were heard by both Hawkins-Smith and Gillford. He said, "It is all my fault."

The court-martial on the loss of the *Victoria*
opened on July 17 at Malta. The court sat for ten
days. It took evidence and, in the end, found that:

The disaster had been caused by the order of
the Commander-in-Chief, Vice-Admiral Sir George
Tryon.

Everything possible had been done to save the
ship and her men.

No blame attached to Captain Maurice Bourke.

The court regretted that Rear Admiral Markham
had not protested more strongly against the fatal
order.

The court said nothing, however, that shed any
light on the baffling mystery of how Admiral Tryon

came to give that order. What was he thinking
What had he intended? He was known to be
master of maneuvers. He was one of the mo
skilled and experienced sailors in the Royal Nav
He was a cool-headed and efficient man. How coul
he have ordered two battleships onto a collisio
course?

There seem to be only two possible explanation

One is that there was something wrong with Tryo
that afternoon. Perhaps, as some naval men of hi
day suggested, he was sick. His mind was cloude
and moving slowly. And so he failed to grasp th
danger of his own order. The officers of his shij
who knew him well, did not think he was sick. Bu
it is still a possibility. Or perhaps he was sufferin
one of those odd mental lapses that affect everyon
from time to time.

For example, it is possible to add up a column o
figures and keep getting the wrong answer. Th
reason is that you are making the same error ove
and over again without realizing it. You keep add
ing 9 and 4 and getting 15, though you know per
fectly well that the sum is 13. Only later do you se
where your error lay. It is possible that Sir Georg
Tryon made just such an error over the distance
between the columns of ships.

Either way, his mind suddenly clear after the col

ision, Tryon saw the dreadful error he had made
nd said, "It is all my fault."

The other possibility is that Tryon had a rather
different maneuver in mind. He may never have
intended the ships to turn in on each other.

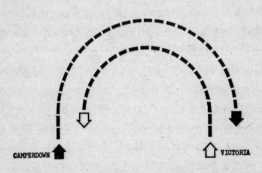

The maneuver as Tryon may have intended it

The signal from the *Victoria* made it clear that
he order of the fleet was to be preserved.

The order of the fleet had the *Victoria* to starboard of the *Camperdown*. If the ships had turned
inward and cleared each other, the *Victoria* would
no longer have been to starboard of the *Camperdown*. She would have been to port.

To preserve the order of the fleet, one ship should
have turned outside the other. In that way, the *Vic-
oria* would still have been to starboard.

Which ship should have gone outside the other?
Regulations of the Royal Navy stated: "If two ship
under steam are crossing so as to involve the risk o
collision, the ship which has the other on her star
board side shall keep out of the way." Therefore, i
was up to the *Camperdown* to keep out of the way

Also, according to naval custom, a commander-in
chief always had the right of way. Other ships wer
not to cross his bows without permission. They wer
to pass the stern. Again, this would mean that th
Camperdown should have circled outside the *Vic
toria*.

Tryon expected his officers to be familiar wit
naval rules. He expected them to think for them
selves. He held each captain responsible for th
safety of his ship. So he may have thought that ther
was only one way the maneuver could be carrie
out. The *Camperdown* would circle outside the *Vic
toria*.

In this case, it made little difference whether th
distance between the columns was six cables o
eight cables. Tryon may have deliberately set it a
six by way of making clear that the ships were *no*
to turn in on each other. Turning inward at si
cables meant certain collision. Surely Markham
would see that and realize what was wanted.

But Markham did not. Neither, for that matter

port **C** starboard → port **V** starboard

To start: *Camperdown* had *Victoria* to starboard

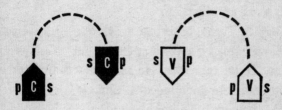

If ships had turned in, *Victoria* would have been to port

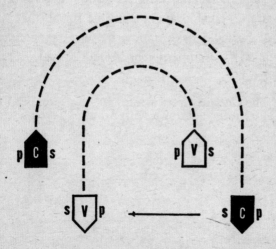

f *Camperdown* had circled outside, she would still have had *Victoria* to starboard

did any of the captains in the fleet. Like Markha
most of them thought the ships were to turn inwar
Like Markham, most of them thought Tryon wou
do something at the last minute to avoid collisio

Perhaps, then, this was Tryon's error: He expecte
too much of Markham.

Unlike Tryon, Markham was not a brilliant ma
He was steady and competent, but cautious a
slow. Tryon knew this. He also knew that Markha
had complete confidence in him.

At the end, the admiral standing on the bridge
his sinking ship may have thought, "So Markha
did not understand after all. But I am the con
mander-in-chief. I am responsible for all that ha
pens. I should have known better. I should hav
watched the *Camperdown*." Aloud he said, "It is a
my fault."

Perhaps.

The truth went down with Admiral Tryon and th
Victoria.

Last Flight

N LATE July, 1936, Amelia Earhart went out to
urbank, California, and began testing the plane
at she proposed to fly around the world.

At the time, she was thirty-eight years old and
ie of the most famous women in the world. She had
een the first woman to fly the Atlantic as a pas-
inger; the first woman to fly solo across the Atlantic;
ie first woman to fly solo from Hawaii to California;
ie first woman to fly solo from California to Mexico
ity; and she was the winner of many aviation
rizes and awards.

Somehow this was not enough. She yearned to do
hat no flier—man or woman—had ever done. She
as tired of being "the first woman to." She wanted
) be "the first flier to." And so she had decided on
round-the-world flight.

Men, it was true, had already flown around the

world. But no flier had yet circled the earth by tl
longest route—at the equator. This was the ta:
Amelia Earhart had set herself.

Her new plane was a twin-engined, all-met
Lockheed Electra. Behind the cockpit, the passeng
seats had been cleared away and two big, ext
fuel tanks bolted to the floor. A navigation roor
with all the latest equipment, lay aft of the fu
tanks.

The series of test flights proved the excellence
the plane. Only one piece of equipment failed
satisfy Miss Earhart. This was the voice radio fc
sending and receiving with ground stations. Wit
a power of fifty watts, its normal range was onl
500 miles. For the ocean legs of the flight she woul
need a much stronger radio, if she was to keep i
touch with the ground.

Miss Earhart tried to borrow a more powerful se
but did not succeed. Finally, she decided to mak
do with what she had. When they were out c
touch with the ground, her navigator would hav
to work with instruments alone.

Meanwhile, her husband, George Palmer Putnan
had been busy with other arrangements for he
flight. He had collected all the charts and weathe
studies she would need. He had applied for th
visas giving her permission to land in foreign cour

Her plane was a twin-engined Lockheed Electra

tries. He had arranged for supplies of fuel and oil at her landing points.

Take-off was planned for mid-March, 1937. Because of weather conditions at that time of year, it was to be an east-west flight, with the first leg California to Hawaii. The flight plan had an added advantage. The most difficult part of the trip would come first, when Miss Earhart was rested and fresh. The Pacific was a vast ocean, dotted at the equator with only tiny specks of land. It was going to require first-rate flying and navigating to find such specks and home in on them for fuel. Later parts of the flight would not be easy. But at least there would be landmarks to guide her. The broad reaches of the Pacific offered no such help.

The size of the Pacific had, in fact, forced her to seek the help of a navigator. She would much have preferred to fly solo around the world.

The navigator she had chosen was an old friend and ship captain, Harry Manning. He would help her with the first four legs of the trip: California to Hawaii; Hawaii to the tiny island of Howland; Howland to New Guinea; New Guinea to Brisbane, Australia. From Brisbane on, Miss Earhart hoped to continue alone.

On March 17, the Electra took off from California. The flight was smooth. Fifteen hours and forty-seven

minutes later, Miss Earhart was touching down at
Honolulu, Hawaii. However, on take-off from
Hawaii, the Electra cracked up on the runway. No
one was hurt, but the Electra needed major re-
pairs. They would not be completed before May.

The delay meant scrapping the flight plan. By
May or June weather conditions on a round-the-
world flight would be completely different. Once-
favorable winds would have become unfavorable.
Rainy seasons would have started in some places
while dust storms replaced rains in others. A west-
east route seemed better for this flight.

The delay also meant a change in navigators.
Captain Manning's leave was up and he had to
return to his ship. To replace him, Miss Earhart
asked Fred Noonan to be her navigator. Noonan
was a veteran of ocean travel, a pilot, and an in-
structor in aerial navigation.

Some of her flying friends, though, were worried
by this change in navigators. They were far from
sure that Noonan could handle the navigation for
the long, overwater legs of the flight. Jacqueline
Cochran, another famous woman flier, suggested a
test. Take Noonan far out over the Pacific, she told
Miss Earhart. Fly him in circles and then see if he
can get you back to Los Angeles.

Miss Earhart took the suggestion. Noonan plotted

the course back. And the Electra came in over California halfway between Los Angeles and San Francisco. With the California coast as a target, the error was not serious. But there were legs in the trip where such an error could be fatal. Howland Island, for example, was a dot of land two miles long, three quarters of a mile wide, and fifteen feet above sea level. Finding it in the Pacific would demand great skill on the part of a navigator.

Still, Miss Earhart kept Noonan on, confident both of his ability and her own.

The time of departure drew near.

At 5:56 A.M. on June 1, 1937, the Electra raced down the runway at Miami, Florida, bound for California by the longest route possible.

The first legs of the flight took them to Puerto Rico, Venezuela, Dutch Guiana, and Brazil. Natal, Brazil, was the take-off point for the long hop across the South Atlantic to Africa. Their destination was Dakar, 1,900 miles away.

The overwater flight went well, except for one incident at the end. Approaching Africa, Miss Earhart overruled her navigator. His directions were to turn right. Instinct told her to turn left. She followed her hunch and less than an hour later found herself 163 miles off course. She had gone north instead of south. Dutifully, she recorded the incident in her logbook.

Ahead lay long and grueling legs of flight across Africa's 4,350 miles. Aviation maps of Africa were poor, and there were no radio beams to home in on. Still, Africa was crossed, then Arabia. On they went to Karachi, Calcutta, Akyab, Rangoon, Bangkok, and Singapore. From Singapore they flew to Bandung, Java, then a Dutch colony. Here one of the most important engine instruments failed. The flight was delayed until Dutch technicians fixed it.

The next leg took them to Surabaya. There navigation instruments failed. Noonan could not get his most important long-range instruments to work. They backtracked to Bandung, where Dutch technicians worked for two days on the navigation instruments.

Finally, they were off again—Koepong, on the island of Timor; Port Darwin, Australia; Lae, New Guinea. They arrived in Lae on June 30.

They had now covered 22,000 miles in a month's time. The long hours of flying and the brief periods of rest snatched here and there were taking their toll. Pilot and navigator were bone-weary. Yet the longest, most difficult leg of the flight was still to come—the 2,556 miles from Lae to Howland. "I shall be glad when we have the hazards of its navigation behind us," Amelia Earhart scribbled in the logbook that she was about to ship home.

Most of this long leg lay over open water. There would be almost no landmarks.

For the first 500 miles out of New Guinea, they could get radio bearings. For the last 500 miles, they could home into Howland on radio signals from the Coast Guard cutter *Itasca*. But for 1,500 miles they would be on their own. Given clear weather, they would use the stars by night and the sun by day for navigating.

Still, if all went well, twenty hours of flying should see Miss Earhart touching down on Howland.

All did not go well. While on New Guinea, they discovered that they were having radio trouble. Because of this, Noonan was not sure whether his chronometers—the time-measuring instruments—were set fast or slow.

Nevertheless, they decided to push ahead. They were so tired that all they really wanted was to finish the flight and get home.

At ten o'clock in the morning, the Electra roared down the runway at Lae. The date was July 2 on New Guinea. Their destination, Howland, lay on the other side of the international date line. So this was, in a way, a flight into yesterday. The date on Howland was July 1.

In the late afternoon, Miss Earhart talked by radio with Lae. She was then directly on course and proceeding to Howland.

That evening at Howland, the *Itasca's* radio equipment was given a final check. Everything was working well.

The arrangements were that the *Itasca* would broadcast the weather on the hour and the half hour. It would also use a telegraph key to send out a long series of A's, the signal that the Electra would home in on. At quarter to and quarter past the hour, Miss Earhart was to report in, using her call letters KHAQQ.

Shortly after midnight the *Itasca* began trying to reach the plane. KHAQQ did not reply. This was not surprising, though. The Electra then was probably about 1,000 miles away and still out of radio range. However, there are times when radio waves skip and travel much longer distances. So the *Itasca* continued to send, on the chance of making contact early.

At 2:45 A.M. KHAQQ came in. Because of static, listeners on the *Itasca* could make out only three words: "Cloudy and overcast."

Encouraged, the *Itasca* tried to talk with Miss

Earhart. The attempt was unsuccessful. She gave no sign of having heard the messages.

At 3:45 Miss Earhart came in again. "*Itasca* from Earhart . . . *Itasca* from Earhart . . . Overcast . . . Will listen on hour and half hour . . . Will listen on hour and half hour. . . . "

At 4:00, on schedule, the *Itasca* gave the weather. Then it asked, "What is your position? When do you expect to arrive at Howland? We are receiving your signals. Please acknowledge this message on your next schedule."

4:15 A.M.: No word from the Electra.

4:30 A.M.: The *Itasca* sent the weather.

4:55 A.M.: KHAQQ called in, but the *Itasca* could not make out what Miss Earhart was saying.

5:30 A.M.: The *Itasca* sent the weather both by voice and key. By key it sent out the homing signal.

5:45 A.M.: No word from Miss Earhart.

6:00 A.M.: The *Itasca* repeated the weather and the homing signal.

6:15 A.M.: Miss Earhart called in. She believed they were about 200 miles from Howland, but she wanted the *Itasca* to check her position. She would whistle into her microphone so that the ship could take a bearing and tell her exactly where she was. But the whistle was lost in static and other radio noises. The *Itasca* could not take a bearing on it.

6:45 A.M.: Miss Earhart called in again. Her voice vas clear and strong. "*Please* take a bearing on us nd report in half an hour," she said. "We are about 00 miles out." Again the *Itasca* could not get a earing, for Miss Earhart did not whistle long nough. Almost an hour passed before she next roke radio silence.

7:42 A.M.: KHAQQ came in, Miss Earhart's voice igh and frantic. "We must be on you," she said. But we cannot see you. Our gas is running low. 3een unable to reach you by radio. We are flying t altitude 1,000 feet."

The *Itasca* acknowledged her message and sent ut the homing signal.

7:49 A.M., *Itasca* to KHAQQ: "Your message O.K. lease acknowledge."

7:58 A.M.: Apparently Miss Earhart had not eard the *Itasca*, for she broke in without acknowl-dging the ship's message. "KHAQQ calling *Itasca*," he said. "We are circling but cannot hear you. Go head either now or on schedule time of half hour."

8:00 A.M.: The *Itasca* sent the homing signal. Miss Earhart replied immediately. She was receiv-ng the signal but could not get a bearing on it. again she asked the *Itasca* to take a bearing on her. again the *Itasca* failed. Her whistling could not be eard clearly enough.

By this time the Electra had been in the air for twenty hours and should have been over Howland.

The *Itasca* continued to call.

8:45 A.M.: The *Itasca* heard Miss Earhart again. Her voice was loud, clear, and anxious. "We are in a line of position 157–337 . . . We are running north and south," she said.

They were her last words.

The *Itasca* continued to call, but the Electra was not heard from again. By noon any possibility of seeing the Electra appear in the sky was gone. The plane could no longer have any fuel.

Amelia Earhart and Fred Noonan were down somewhere in the South Pacific.

The United States Navy, determined to find them, set in motion the start of a great search.

The Navy believed that Miss Earhart had come down within a few hundred miles of Howland. The strength of her last radio signals indicated that she was then between thirty and 250 miles from Howland. A check of weather reports convinced the Navy that she was probably to the north of Howland. Her radio messages had been full of static, and there had been thunderstorms to the north.

The *Itasca* steamed north to start the search. Hopes were high that the cutter would find the downed plane quickly. According to Lockheed, the

lane could float for at least nine hours in the water.
f it began to sink, the two fliers had a life raft, life
ackets, flares—everything they would need.

The *Itasca* sent up a thick smoke screen so that
he fliers could see the ship from afar and signal.
Vhen night came, the cutter played its searchlights
gainst the sky, while crewmen kept a constant
vatch for flares.

No trace was found of the two fliers. There was
o sign of the plane, a raft, or wreckage. The watch
aw no flares and heard no signal guns.

The days passed. The *Itasca* combed the area
vithout success.

Meanwhile, other ships were steaming full speed
oward Howland to help with the search. On July
the battleship *Colorado* and the mine sweeper
wan joined the *Itasca*. Two days later the aircraft
arrier *Lexington*, with sixty-three planes, sailed
rom Hawaii. So did four destroyers.

As the search became broader and broader, the
Javy once more reviewed the few known facts.

It was known that the Electra had had radio
rouble. Noonan had had trouble with the naviga-
ion instruments. At 2:45 A.M. on July 2, Miss Ear-
aart had reported the weather as cloudy and over-
ast. There was no telling whether Noonan had
een able to see the stars that night. If he hadn't,

then they must have flown by compass alone. And
tiny compass error would grow into a big direction
error during such a long flight.

Added up, the known facts told the Navy onl
one thing: The two fliers could be anywhere withi
twenty flying hours of Lae.

The last message from the Electra did not clarif
matters. No one was sure what Miss Earhart ha
meant by "line of position 157–337." Probably
was a sun line, but a sun line is meaningless withou
a point of geographical reference. Her "we are run
ning north and south" meant that she was conduct
ing a search pattern for Howland or some othe
speck of land. It meant she did not know where sh
was.

For sixteen days ships and planes searched mor
than 250,000 square miles of the Pacific.

Toward the end, two lookouts and an office
aboard one of the ships saw what looked like a gree
flare to the north. The Itasca immediately swep
north to investigate. There was still some hope tha
the Electra had come down on land and that Mis
Earhart could receive radio messages. So the Itasc
called her and asked whether she was sending u
flares. If she was, the Itasca wanted her to send u
another. A minute later another green light wa
seen by twenty-five men aboard the cutter. How

ver, other ships in the area saw nothing. Their fficers warned the *Itasca* that the lights were probbly heat lightning.

At another time, Howland thought it saw flares the northeast. The *Swan* also saw lights, but ought they were meteors.

In any case, the missing fliers were not found. nd, at last, the Navy called off the search.

Amelia Earhart and Fred Noonan were missing nd presumed lost. There was not the slightest clue s to where they had gone down or what had happened to them.

Rumors now sprang into life, accounting for the ysterious loss of the two fliers.

Most of the rumors had to do with the Japanese. the late 1930's the Japanese were secretly prearing for war. They were fortifying islands in the acific and permitted no outsiders to see what they ere doing.

One story claimed that Miss Earhart and Noonan ad flown over such an island and been shot down. oth had been taken prisoner and jailed as spies.

That story is still told today, chiefly because of a ovie made in the 1940's. The movie told of a mous woman flier who had "vanished" at the reuest of the United States Navy during a flight over e Pacific. The movie heroine was actually in hid-

ing at Howland. But her "disappearance" gave th
Navy an excuse to photograph the Japanese island
while "looking" for her. Over the years many peop
have confused the movie story with the facts.

Yet, curiously, that was the story Amelia Earhart
mother long believed. She insisted that her daugh
ter had been on a secret mission and had been ca
tured by the Japanese.

The Navy has denied the story. No clue poin
to its being true. But the story lives on.

Another story had Miss Earhart crash landing i
the Marshall Islands, which are considerably nor
and west of Howland. The witness in this story wa
a native who had been trained by missionaries. H
said he had seen the plane come down, seen
Japanese fishing boat pick up an American woma
seen the boat head off to Japan.

A third story centered on the island of Saipa
According to this story, Miss Earhart and Noona
made a forced landing in the harbor at Saipa
There they were arrested by Japanese soldiers, le
off, and executed. The Japanese have official
denied that this happened. Yet this particular stor
has turned up time and again.

It was, for example, revived in the summer c
1960. A team of CBS reporters had gone to Saipa
to investigate this old rumor. They came back wit

cordings of testimony by a number of witnesses.
ne witnesses, all natives of Saipan, agreed that
ey had seen a plane come down in their harbor
iring the summer of 1937. They had seen a white
oman and a man get out of the plane. They had
en Japanese soldiers take the couple away. Most
them later heard that the white couple had been
ecuted. One witness even said that he had been
vited to see a white woman hanged, but had
fused to go.

The investigators brought back parts of a plane
und on the harbor bottom at Saipan. The gen-
ator was sent to Bendix to see if this was the one
e company had made for Miss Earhart's plane.

About the same time, an Air Force captain was
ported to have photographs proving that the two
ers had been executed on Saipan. He also claimed
have sworn statements from seventy-two wit-
esses that this had happened. And he said he had
und the place where Amelia Earhart and Fred
oonan were buried.

Once more, the story petered out.

Nothing more has been heard of the captain's
port.

Bendix said the generator was not from Miss Ear-
rt's plane. Its serial number was different.

As for the witnesses, their testimony may or may

not have been true. Perhaps they did see Miss Ea
hart and her navigator. Perhaps they have simpl
come to believe that they did. There are many suc
cases on record. An exciting event takes plac
Everyone talks about it. Twenty or more years g
by. And presently people begin to think they wi
nessed the event. The picture is so clear in the
minds that they truly believe they saw somethin
they did not see. This may well be the case o
Saipan.

For it is not easy to believe that Miss Earha
flew to Saipan instead of Howland.

Saipan and Howland are both some 2,550 mile
from Lae. But they lie in completely different dire
tions. Howland is east of New Guinea; Saipan
north.

If Miss Earhart crash landed at Saipan, thre
highly unlikely things must have happened:

First, there was a tremendous error in navigation
Soon after speaking with Lae, the Electra left th
east-bound course and turned north and wes
Either Miss Earhart was ignoring her compass o
she misread it by 100 degrees. This is almost un
believable.

Second, Noonan must have done no navigatin
at all during the night.

Third, conditions must have been such that radi

waves were skipping for extremely long distances. Otherwise Miss Earhart, approaching Saipan, could not possibly have talked with the *Itasca* at Howland.

For these reasons, a landing at Saipan is unlikely. It does, however, remain possible. Radio waves do sometimes skip. Noonan may not have been able to see the stars. And Miss Earhart once before on this flight followed her own instincts instead of her navigator's directions.

The two fliers came down somewhere in the South Pacific. If they were near Howland, the Navy ought to have found them. The Navy did not. Perhaps the Navy failed. Perhaps the fliers were not there to be found. It is impossible to tell.

There is no solution to the mystery of Amelia Earhart's last flight. It is only certain that, in the long night flight toward a tiny speck of land, she was somehow defeated by the vastness of the Pacific. The ocean claimed the plane that soared above it, just as it has claimed the many ships and men who have vanished from its surface.